IDEAL
SOLOS – DUETS
FOR
GOSPEL SINGERS

A Collection of Excellent and Interesting Sacred Selections

Compiled and Edited by

C. Austin Miles

The RODEHEAVER *Co.*

HALL-MACK

WINONA LAKE, INDIANA

Printed in U. S. A.

DEDICATION

From thousands of manuscripts the finest have been selected for the making of IDEAL SOLOS-DUETS FOR GOSPEL SINGERS.

In addition many hours of research revealed choice selections already published to secure which would require the expenditure of a large sum for various books necessary. To gather all these in one volume and sell for a reasonable price to Gospel Singers seemed desirable; indeed, repeated requests for a book of this kind could no longer be ignored.

It is certain that there are many deeply devoted to Christian work who appreciate the value of a Gospel message in song and who earnestly desire to present the message in that form. To them this book is respectfully dedicated.

THE PUBLISHER.

SUGGESTIONS

Those who are experienced in Gospel song work know the necessity for proper preparation. They study the words carefully and endeavor to interpret the composition according to its meaning.

Consider each word, line and verse as a separate unit and adapt the musical accent thereto, without regard to strict time. The message *must* appeal to the singer if it is to reach the heart of the listener.

Ideal Solos-Duets
For Gospel Singers.

No. 1. **When He Held Out His Hands.**

HAROLD G. ASH.

RUTH E. BLOSE.

1. When Je-sus was nailed to Calv'ry's tree He held out His hands to be pierced for me;
2. You won-der just why I love Him so, You wonder just why to my Je-sus I go;
3. I'll nev-er re-ject such wondrous love For God sent His Son to redeem from a-bove;

What anguish and pain in His heart must have reigned, When He held out His hands for me.
From sin I'm released in my heart there is peace, Since He held out His hands for me.
From wounds flowed the blood o'er my heart rolled its flood When He held out His hands for me.

REFRAIN.

When He held out His hands for me,...... When He held out His hands for me;........

They were nailed for me to an old rugged tree, When He held out His hands for me.

I See Thy Hand.

D. K. W.

C. Austin Miles.

un poco accel.

1. Thro' bright-est day and dark-est night,...... Thro' ev - 'ry gift that greets the sight;............ Thro' joy or sor - row, toil or pain, Thro' ev - 'ry rich - es
2. Thro' love of mother, sweetheart, friend,...... Thro' count - less gifts that nev-er end;............ Thro' life, thro' death, thro' earth, thro' sky, Thro' prom - is - es that
3. Thro' this short space of earth-ly bloom,...... Thro' all the si-lence of the tomb;............ Thro' pearl - y gates to gold-en shores, Thro' earth - ly cares then

rit.

Refrain. *a tempo con espress.*

I at - tain; }
nev - er die; } I see Thy hand,......... I see Thy
to be o'er; }

rit.

hand, In prom - is-es that nev - er die I see Thy hand.

rall.

No. 3.

Don't Worry.

John Bieri.

Rev. John Bieri, D. D.

1. When the He-brews fled from Pha-roah in dis-may, With a trembling heart they
2. When they wandered in the des-ert with-out bread, With sweet manna from the
3. When they reached the banks where Jordan's waters flow, When they faced the mighty
4. You may wan-der thro' the val-ley with its gloom, Fier-y trials and pris-ons

faced the Red Sea's spray; But their lead-er said, march on, do not de-lay, Don't
skies they all were fed, And they found each morning's ta-ble rich-ly spread: Don't
walls of Jer-i-cho, God was there His sav-ing pow-er to be-stow: Don't
dark may threaten doom, Not a soul on earth may care to give you room, Don't

Chorus.

wor-ry for the Lord will see you thro'. Don't wor-ry for the Lord will see you

thro', Re-mem-ber that He'll be a friend to you, For He whispers "Do not

fear, I will fill your heart with cheer," Don't worry for the Lord will see you thro'.

No. 4. Wonderful Friend.

Rev. Oswald J. Smith.

B. D. Ackley.

1. Won-der-ful Friend, Won-der-ful Friend, Je-sus who died for me;
2. Won-der-ful joy, won-der-ful joy, Je-sus has giv-en me;
3. Won-der-ful peace, won-der-ful peace, Fath-om-less as the sea;
4. Won-der-ful life, won-der-ful life Je-sus has brought to me;

Won-der-ful Friend, Won-der-ful Friend, Tru-est of friends is He;
Won-der-ful joy, won-der-ful joy, Boundless and full and free.
Won-der-ful peace, won-der-ful peace, Je-sus is all to me.
Won-der-ful life, won-der-ful life, Mine, thro' e-ter-ni-ty.

REFRAIN.

Won-der-ful, won-der-ful Sav-iour! Faith-ful and lov-ing is He,

Won-der-ful, won-der-ful Sav-iour! Mine, thro' e-ter-ni-ty!

Before the King.

C. AUSTIN MILES.

J. LINCOLN HALL.

DUET.

1. When my last word I have writ - ten, When my fin - al note I
2. Sweet the com - fort is in know - ing There is noth - ing I need
3. I shall pass from "here" to "yon - der" And shall not need an - y -

sing, I shall pass thro' heav - en's por - tal There to
bring; All of earth I'll leave be - hind me, When I
thing But the pres - ence of my Sav - iour As we

stand be - fore the King. There is One.............. who will be
There is One

close to me, To His hand.............. by faith I cling,......... And I
To His hand

know He will speak for me When I stand be - fore the King.

No. 6. The Hand That Turns the Clouds to Gold.

Augusta C. Anderson (Words and Melody.)

Arr. by Evelyn Sibelius.

Solo or Duet.

1. What though it lead through des - ert sand, The jour - ney
2. And if a tear should dim my sight, I know that
3. And when at last I near the shore, My jour - ney's

to my Father's land; I'll fear no night tho' stars may hide,
Je - sus is my Light; Though dim - ly here thro' veils I see,
joys and sor-rows o'er, I'll join with heaven's hosts in praise,

REFRAIN.

Be - hind the clouds, when Je - sus is my Guide.
I know my Sav - iour's hand will pi - lot me. } I'll take that
To Him who guid - ed me in all my ways.

Hand, nail-pierced for me, To lead me on and keep me free; I

rit. *pp*

know..... whose hand I hold, It is the Hand whose touch turns clouds to gold.

'Tis Jesus.

A. P. Bowen.

Adam Geibel.

1. Some-one be-held me a soul lost in sin, Came to my res-cue, and
2. Some-one, tho' wea-ry and heart-sick, one day Plead with the Fa-ther man's
3. Some-one is guard-ing my foot-steps to-day, Ten-der-ly watch-ing lest
4. Some-one is keep-ing a crown I shall wear When I thro' grace, heav'nly

I was for-giv'n; Some-one who knew all the beau-ties of heav'n—
sen-tence to stay; Some-one who died my re-demp-tion to pay—
I go a-stray; Some-one who's guid-ing me o-ver life's way—
man-sions shall share; Some-one who knows how I long to be there—

CHORUS.

Some-one who loves me— 'tis Je- sus. Some-one whose love is far

bet-ter than gold, Some one whose love ne'er can ful-ly be told;

Down thro' the a-ges the mes-sage has roll'd, "Somebody loves me"—'tis Je-sus.

No. 8. I Wonder Why?

Lizzie DeArmond.

C. Austin Miles.

1. I won-der why the Lord of all, Stoops down from heav'n to hear my call?
2. I won-der why the King di-vine, Should say He was a friend of mine?
3. I won-der why on Cal-va-ry, My Sav-iour died to ran-som me?

No good to me will He de-ny, I won-der why, I won-der why?
He will not leave nor pass me by, I won-der why, I won-der why?
Still to my soul He's ev-er nigh I won-der why, I won-der why?

REFRAIN.

For love He came,.................. O bless His name! On
For love He came, O bless His name!

Cal-va-ry con-tent to die; Thro' grace di-vine,.............. this friend is
Thro' grace di-vine,

mine, is mine, No lon-ger will I won-der why.

No. 9.

Thou Keepest Thine Own.

C. A. M.

C. AUSTIN MILES.

Slowly.

1. O how mar-vel-lous! O how won-der-ful! Is Thy love, O Christ, for me;
2. Love that sat-is-fies, love that glo-ri-fies All the work of grace be-gun;
3. All e-ter-ni-ty I shall ev-er be, Sing-ing of Thy love and grace,

Ev-er keep-ing me, ev-er lead-ing me In a way I may not see.
In a yield-ed heart, of Thine own a part, Ev-en Thine, O bless-ed Son.
That has purchased me, O so full and free, Near Thy throne a rest-ing place.

* REFRAIN. *Reverently.*

I am { tru-ly Thine, dear Lord, "So all un-worth-y Thee
{ aught of worth in me, It comes from Thee a-lone;
dear Lord, in me,

[1]
That the dust up-on Thy feet, Out-weighs me ut-ter-ly. If there's
Thy feet.

[2]
rit.
Then keep me safe, for so, O Lord, Thou keep-est but Thine own."

* From poem by N. V. Tilak.

No One Ever Cared for Me Like Jesus.

C. F. WEIGLE.

1. I would love to tell you what I think of Je - sus
2. All my life was full of sin when Je - sus found me,
3. Ev - 'ry day He comes to me with new as - sur - ance,

Since I found in Him a friend so strong and true; I would
All my heart was full of mis - er - y and woe; Je - sus
More and more I un - der - stand His words of love; But I'll

tell you how He changed my life com - plete - ly, He did something that no
plac'd His strong and lov - ing arms a - bout me, And He led me in the
nev - er know just why He came to save me, Till some day I see His

CHORUS.

oth - er friend could do.
way I ought to go.   } No one ev - er cared for me like Je - sus,
bless - ed face a - bove.

There's no oth - er friend so kind as He; No one else could take the

No One Ever Cared for Me, etc.—Concluded.

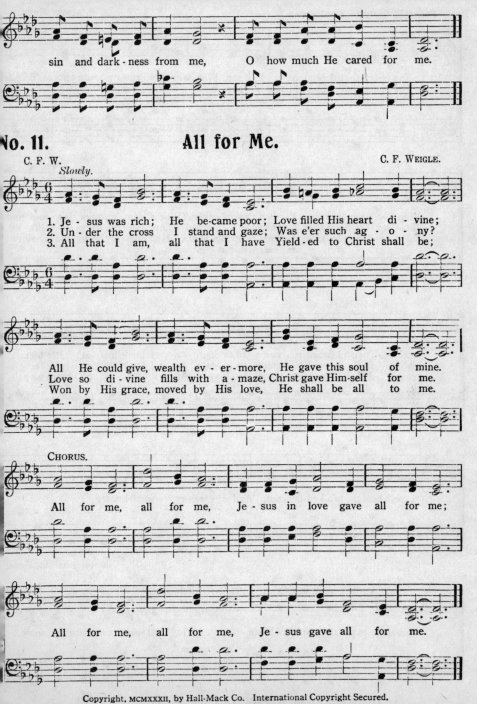

sin and dark-ness from me, O how much He cared for me.

No. 11.   All for Me.

C. F. W.

C. F. WEIGLE.

Slowly.

1. Je - sus was rich; He be-came poor; Love filled His heart di - vine;
2. Un - der the cross I stand and gaze; Was e'er such ag - o - ny?
3. All that I am, all that I have Yield-ed to Christ shall be;

All He could give, wealth ev - er-more, He gave this soul of mine.
Love so di - vine fills with a - maze, Christ gave Him-self for me.
Won by His grace, moved by His love, He shall be all to me.

CHORUS.

All for me, all for me, Je - sus in love gave all for me;

All for me, all for me, Je - sus gave all for me.

No. 12.   The Heart I Brought to Jesus.

FRANK E. GRAEFF. (Posthumous.)   C. AUSTIN MILES.

1. The heart that I brought to Je - sus Was wea - ry and so sore oppress'd; And
2. The heart that I brought to Je - sus Was sin - ful and of crim - son dye; And
3. The heart that I bring to Je - sus Is bless - ed now and full of peace; And

man - y the tears that I shed as I asked, "Where can a seek - ing soul find
bit - ter the tears that I shed as I prayed Low at the cross up - lift - ed
ho - ly the joy that is flood - ing my soul, Hap - py my song that shall not

rest?" Then I heard His voice so sweet, As I knelt low at His feet:
high: Still I heard His voice so sweet, As I knelt low at His feet:
cease; For I hear His voice to - day All a - long my pil - grim way:

REFRAIN.

"I will heal the bro - ken - hearted, And the wea - ry rest shall know;

the weary rest shall know;

rit.

And the heart all stain'd and sin - ful I will wash as white as snow."

No. 13.

If.

Anon.

C. Austin Miles.

1. If we could see be-yond to-day As God can see; If all the clouds should roll a-way, The shad-ows flee; O'er pres-ent griefs we would not fret, Each sor-row we would soon for-get; For man-y joys are wait-ing yet, For you and me.

2. If we could know be-yond to-day As God doth know, Why dear-est treas-ures pass a-way, And tears must flow, And why the darkness leads to light, Why drear-y paths will soon grow bright; Some day life's wrongs will be made right, Faith tells us so.

3. "If we could see, if we could know," We oft-en say; But God in love a veil doth throw A-cross our way: We can-not see what lies be-fore, And so we cling to Him the more, He leads us 'til this life is o'er—Trust (Omit.......................) and o-bey.

cresc. e accel.

a tempo.

rit.

1st and 2d verses. | Third verse.

No. 14. Fair Sharon's Rose.

C. Austin Miles.   Norman Roy.

1. There was a rose in Shar-on grow-ing, That must have been of wondrous
2. With-in my heart there is a gar-den, And Shar-on's Rose is blooming
3. O take the Rose of Shar-on with you, With grace and love so rich and

fame; Else, how could He who walked a-mong them Be hon-ored by its name?
there, For He who is the Rose of Shar-on My dai-ly life doth share.
fair; Your life will grow in full-est meas-ure If Christ be dwelling there.

REFRAIN.

O { Rose......... of Shar-on fair, Come, bloom...... with-in my
  { grace...... no tongue can tell, Thy love......... no end-ing
  { Rose, O Rose of Shar-on fair, come dwell with -
  { grace, thy grace no tongue can tell. thy love, no

heart, That I may of Thy beau-ty share, And of Thee
knows, O come with-in my heart to (Omit...................
  in my heart,
  end-ing knows,

be a part, (be a part,) Thy dwell, (to dwell, Fair Shar-on's Rose.

A Friend Above All Others.

Rev. A. H. ACKLEY.

B. D. ACKLEY.

1. He's a Friend a - bove all oth - - - ers, None like Him can un - der - stand,............ When I need a heart to pi - ty, When I need a help - ing hand............

2. He's a Friend a - bove all oth - - - ers, Though un - seen yet not un - known, ... Far more real than friends a - round me, That I see and call my own. ....

3. He's a Friend a - bove all oth - - - ers, Who, like Him, can keep my life?................ Who de - fend me in the con - - flict, Who give vic - to - ry in strife? ....

CHORUS.

He's a Friend a - bove all oth - ers,
a - bove all oth - ers,
Tow'r-ing high a - bove them all;

Je - sus nev - er fails to hear me,
to hear me,
And to an - swer when I call.

Come, Rest Awhile.

"Come ye yourselves apart and rest awhile."—Mark 6: 31.

C. A. M.

C. Austin Miles.

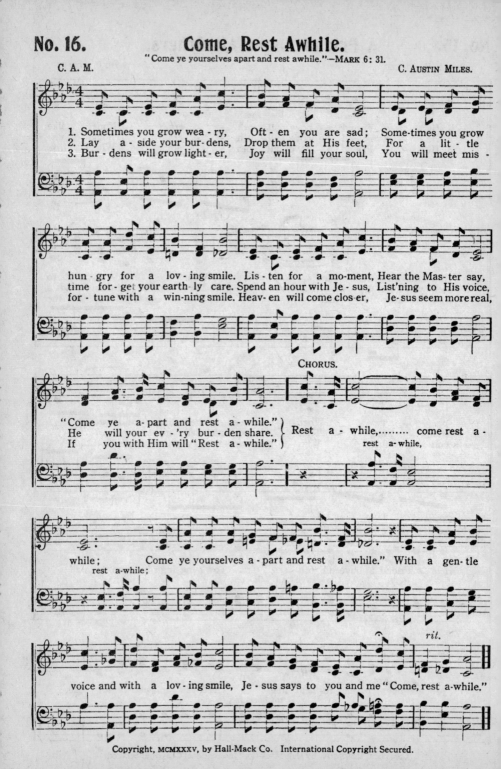

1. Sometimes you grow wea - ry, Oft - en you are sad; Some-times you grow
2. Lay a - side your bur-dens, Drop them at His feet, For a lit - tle
3. Bur - dens will grow light - er, Joy will fill your soul, You will meet mis -

hun - gry for a lov-ing smile. Lis - ten for a mo-ment, Hear the Mas - ter say,
time for-get your earth-ly care. Spend an hour with Je - sus, List'ning to His voice,
for - tune with a win-ning smile. Heav-en will come clos-er, Je-sus seem more real,

CHORUS.

"Come ye a-part and rest a-while."
He will your ev-'ry bur-den share. Rest a-while,......... come rest a-
If you with Him will "Rest a-while."
rest a-while,

while; Come ye yourselves a-part and rest a-while." With a gen-tle
rest a-while;

voice and with a lov-ing smile, Je-sus says to you and me "Come, rest a-while."

rit.

No. 17   A Loving Heart.

Written for and Dedicated to James A. Mason.

C. Austin Miles.   Clinton D. Lowden.

1. 'Mid the throng in which I'm dai - ly liv - ing There must be one who needs a ten - der word; Be it mine, the ho - ly joy of giv - ing That to - ken in the name of Christ, my Lord.........
2. Lov - ing hearts that beat in hap - py un - ion With those who need a mes - sage from a - bove. Are not gained ex - cept from sweet com - mun - ion With Him whose heart still o - ver - flows with love...........
3. High and low may seek and sure - ly find Him; He trav - els best who jour - neys with the Lord, Blest the bonds that to the Sav - iour bind Him As they to - geth - er walk in one ac - cord.........

Chorus.

{ Give me, O Lord,............ a lov - ing heart............ That reaches out to touch a
{ His burden bear,............ His sor-row share;........ (*Omit*................

1. Give me, O Lord, a lov-ing heart

soul with love di - vine, ... Give me a lov - ing heart, dear Lord, like Thine.

No. 18. Jesus, My Friend.

Rev. Howard King Williams, D.D. Elmer A. Naylor.

1. As eve-ning shad-ows fall on the sea, Thoughts of my Mas-ter
2. In life's dark hour He lin-gers with me, With love and pit-y
3. Sweet mys-ter-y of blue Gal-i-lee, True Son of Man and
4. I can-not know the half of His love, Born of the heav'n-ly

steal o-ver me, Bath-ing my soul in sweet mys-ter-y; O
He sets me free; Bids me look up His kind face to see,— O
God is He, Reach-ing the low-est depths of my sin, Yet
Fa-ther a-bove; Yet I may have Him till life shall end,

REFRAIN.

Man of Gal-i-lee...............
Christ of Gal-i-lee............... } He is with me
touch-ing heav-en's rim...............
Je-sus, Je-sus, my Friend.........

by night and day, Walk-ing with me all of my way;

With me un-til life's road shall end, Je-sus, Je-sus, my Friend......

* Play throughout as indicated in first two measures. Melody in lower notes.

Beyond the Mist.

JAMES ROWE.

B. D. ACKLEY.

SOLO OR DUET.

1. Be - yond the mist and gloom of life,............... Be - yond the
2. Be - yond the mist, those gone be - fore .... Are wait - ing
3. Be - yond the mist, in fade - less light,............... My faith will

reach of sin and strife;........... Be - side a calm e - ter - nal
on the gold - en shore;........... And O the joy to know that
end in per - fect sight, ... And I shall clasp His hand and

sea,........ There is a home prepared for me.
they .... Will welcome me some bet - ter day! }
see......... The matchless Friend who died for me! }

REFRAIN.

There I shall sing a

glad new song, And min - gle with the hap - py throng, Of friends and

loved ones gone be - fore, To praise my God for ev - er more.

No. 20. The Living Spring.

Oroville L. Snow.

Haldor Lillenas.

BARITONE SOLO AND CHORUS.

1. I wandered man-y years in sin, On des-erts wild and bare;......... I
2. I chased the bright winged butterflies, And guild-ed toys of earth;...... But
3. I gave my wea-ry wand'ring o'er, And came to Christ my Lord;........ He

sought in vain some cool-ing spring, To quench my thirsting there............
when I reached to grasp the prize, It proved of lit-tle worth............
is my Guide and Coun-se-lor, My joy and my re-ward...... .....

CHORUS.

I've found an ev-er liv-ing spring That sat-is-fies my soul;.........

And 'neath its heal-ing flood I sing Of Him who makes me whole;......
makes me whole;

The Living Spring.—Concluded.

And 'neath its heal-ing flood I sing Of Him who makes me whole...... makes me whole.

No. 21. Unafraid.

Rev. A. H. ACKLEY.

B. D. ACKLEY.

1. Lord, in these days of bit-ter strife,, When all the world with hate is rife,
2. The sounds of tu-mult fill the air, And hope gives way to dark de-spair;
3. Though dark the way of life ap-pears, Be-set with blinding doubts and fears,
4. No mat-ter what the test may be, Help me to walk with spir-it free,

Im-part to me Thy kind-ly life, And keep me un-a-fraid..........
Teach me Thy pa-tient faith to share, And keep me un-a-fraid..........
Fill my cold heart with love for Thee, And keep me un-a-fraid..........
O make me strong to face the wrong, And keep me un-a-fraid..........

CHORUS.

Keep me un-a-fraid, keep me un-a-fraid, O

make me strong to face the wrong And keep me un-a-fraid.

No. 22. A Rainbow of Hope.

Stella Atkinson.

Gertrude Patrick.

Intro.

Solo or Duet. *Con espress.*

1. Do the sor-rows of life seem too heav-y to bear? Is your heart all but
2. When dark o'er our path-way the murk-y clouds low'r, O let us not

bro-ken with grief and despair? There is One up-on whom we can cast ev'ry
question God's wis-dom and pow'r, But im-plic-it-ly trust Him, our ref-uge and

rit. *a tempo.*

care, For He cares for you, cease re-pin-ing When life's fond-est hopes and de-
tow'r, To His ho-ly will full re-sign-ing, When crushed lie the hopes and am-

sire is blight-ed, When by earth-ly friends oft we seem to be slighted, Re-
bi-tions of years, Look up to the One who can calm all your fears, And

A Rainbow of Hope.—Concluded.

member that some day each wrong may be righted, Each cloud has its bright silver lin-ing.
then you shall see thro' the mists of your tears God's rainbow of hope ev-er shin-ing.

No. 23. No Shadows There.

RALPH BUNSEN.

B. D. ACKLEY.

Slow, with expression.

1. There shall be no drear-y shad-ows, For there are no shad-ows there;
2. There shall be no tears of sor-row, For there are no tear-drops there;
3. There shall be no sad a-wake-ning, When in death we fall a-sleep,
4. Thers shall be no pain of part-ing, For there are no part-ings there;

Wea-ry nights of anx-ious wait-ing, End with heav-en's morn-ing fair.
Ev-'ry eye is bright with glad-ness, Joys un-meas-ured ev-'ry-where.
We shall wak-en in His like-ness, Sing-ing, as we up-ward sweep.
Home at last with them for-ev-er, Heav-en's joys with Christ to share.

REFRAIN.

God shall wipe a-way our tears, Qui-et all our doubts and fears,

Heav-en's sky is al-ways fair For there are no shad-ows there.

No. 24. Jesus, the Wonderful Saviour.

O. O.

Oscar Oliver.

BARITONE SOLO AND CHORUS.

1. The Lord is my Shep-herd, I shall not want, He cares for my ev-'ry
2. Though I must pass thro' the val-ley of death, O why should I doubt or
3. My soul is re-stored, my cup run-neth o'er, And noth-ing from Him shall

need,......... In pas-tures green He lead-eth me, For He is a
fear;......... Thy rod and staff they com-fort me, Thy pres-ence is
sev-er; My days on earth are filled with peace, I'll dwell in His

Shep-herd in - deed.........
al - ways so near.......... ⎬
house for - ev - er. ⎭

CHORUS.

Je - sus, the won-der-ful Shep - herd,
won-der - ful Shep - herd,

Great - er none oth - er could be;................ O'er val - ley or steep,
none oth - er could be;

He's seek - ing His sheep, What a won - der - ful Shep-herd is He!

That Glad Day.

C. Austin Miles.

Clinton D. Lowden.

Solo. *Third verse joyfully.*

1. O they nailed Him to the tree, One sad day......... To a cold and cru-el tree,
2. And the sun beheld the sight, One sad day;........ And re-fused to give his light,
3. But there came a glorious morn, One glad day, ... To the sad and the for-lorn,

One sad day. And they watched Him dying there, None to pity, none to care, Left Him
On that day: Then it thundered overhead, And the graves gave up their dead, Many
Bless-ed day! When the sun shone o-verhead, And the tomb gave up its dead :–Christ a-

rit.

CHORUS.

dy - ing in de- spair, One sad day.
hearts were filled with dread On that day.
rose, our Liv - ing Head That glad day.

O they nailed Him to the tree,

There on Cal - va - ry, Where for you and me Je-sus died. Not for

aught that He had done, God's be-lov - ed Son On a cross was cru - ci - fied.

No. 26 — Satisfied.

MATTIE B. SHANNON.
SOLO. *Ad lib.*

ADAM GEIBEL.

1. When the cross that God my Fa-ther gives So ver-y heav-y seems, And
when I see the blighting Find the ash-es of my dreams; When the heart that beats with-
in my breast Is wea-ry and cast down, And when the sun is shadowed, While the
heav-en's seem to frown;

2. When the treas-ures I have striv-en for Are slip-ping fast a-way; When
e-vil tempts me sore-ly And so anx-ious is my day; When the fier-y darts that
Sa-tan sends Are crowding thick and fast, And when youth's hopes are shattered And lie
dy-ing in the blast;

3. When the cares and tri-als of this life Are press-ing more and more; When
death's dark an-gel soft-ly Spreads his wings above my door; When the paths that e'er my
feet must tread So dark and drear-y grow, And when my soul is heav-y With a
name-less pain and woe;

CHORUS.

O I think of Christ my Sav-iour, And the cross on Calv'ry's side, I think of what He bore for me, And am straightway sat-is-fied.

No. 27. When the Little Lost Sheep Comes Home.

CLARA E. PUTNAM.
UNISON OR DUET.

C. AUSTIN MILES.

1. In - to the val - ley of grief and shame, In - to the twi - light dim,
2. White is the fleece of the nine - ty and nine, Mur - mur ye not in scorn,
3. You were a lit - tle lost sheep a - stray, Broth - er, and so was I.

rit.

O - ver the mountain the Shepherd came And gathered His own to Him. . . . .
"Lit - tle Lost Sheep, this coat of thine Is blackened and soiled and torn." . . . .
Wounded and sick on the hills a - way, And read - y al - most to die. . . . . .

a tempo.

What of the nine - ty and nine as - leep And safe while the wild winds
Ten - der the love in the Shep-herd's voice, The quiv - er - ing soul is
On - ly the Shep-herd our souls can keep, Our feet are so prone to

moan? Will they be kind to the lit - tle lost sheep When the
blest; "Heav - en - ly an - gels, re - joice, re - joice! For my
roam; Will you be kind to the lit - tle lost sheep When the

lit - tle lost sheep comes home? When the lit - tle lost sheep comes home?
lit - tle lost sheep can rest, For my lit - tle lost sheep can rest."
lit - tle lost sheep comes home? When the lit - tle lost sheep comes home?

God Has a Garden.

Rev. A. H. ACKLEY.

B. D. ACKLEY.

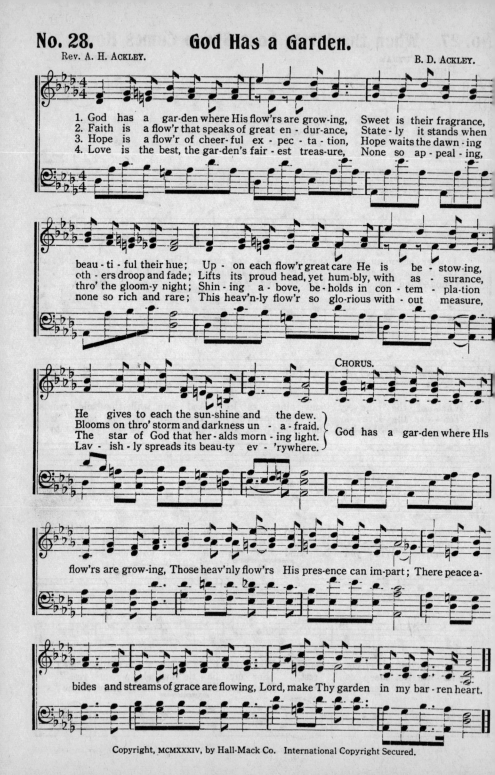

1. God has a gar-den where His flow'rs are grow-ing, Sweet is their fragrance,
2. Faith is a flow'r that speaks of great en - dur-ance, State - ly it stands when
3. Hope is a flow'r of cheer-ful ex - pec - ta - tion, Hope waits the dawn - ing
4. Love is the best, the gar-den's fair - est treas-ure, None so ap - peal - ing,

beau - ti - ful their hue; Up - on each flow'r great care He is be - stow-ing,
oth - ers droop and fade; Lifts its proud head, yet hum-bly, with as - surance,
thro' the gloom-y night; Shin - ing a - bove, be - holds in con - tem - pla-tion
none so rich and rare; This heav'n-ly flow'r so glo-rious with - out measure,

CHORUS.

He gives to each the sun-shine and the dew.
Blooms on thro' storm and darkness un - a - fraid.
The star of God that her - alds morn - ing light. } God has a gar-den where His
Lav - ish - ly spreads its beau-ty ev - 'rywhere.

flow'rs are grow-ing, Those heav'nly flow'rs His pres-ence can im-part; There peace a-

bides and streams of grace are flowing, Lord, make Thy garden in my bar - ren heart.

No. 29.
Why Did They Treat Him So?

C. A. M.

C. Austin Miles.

1. Betrayed with a kiss, by sil - ver bought, By one whom He long had known,
2. They wove Him a crown of thorns to wear, And press'd it up - on His head,
3. They nail'd Him up - on a cross to die And pierc'd with a spear His side,

The Sav - iour of men to Pi - late brought, Was left by His friends, a - lone.
A robe and a scep - tre, too, to bear Ere He to the cross was led.
And there on that cross for such as I The suf - fer - ing Sav - iour died.

REFRAIN.

Why did they treat Him so, Him, who no sin could know? What meant that crown of

thorns He wore? What meant that heav - y cross He bore? Tell me, my soul, if

rall.

thou dost know, Why did they treat Him so? How *could* they treat Him so?

No. 30. Some Bright Morning.

CHARLOTTE G. HOMER.   CHAS. M. GABRIEL.

1. Be not a-wea-ry, for la-bor will cease Some glad morn-ing;
2. Wea-ri-some bur-dens will all be laid down, Some glad morn-ing;
3. La-bor well done shall re-ceive its re-ward, Some glad morn-ing;
4. Oh, what a time of re-joic-ing will come, Some glad morn-ing!

Tur-moil will change in-to in-fi-nite peace, Some bright morn-ing.
Then shall our cross be exchanged for a crown, Some bright morn-ing.
Thou who art faith-ful shalt be with the Lord, Some bright morn-ing.
When all the ransomed are gath-ered at home, Some bright morn-ing.

CHORUS.

Some bright morning. Some glad morn-ing, When the sun is shin-ing

in th' e-ter-nal sky;...... Some bright morn-ing, Some glad

cres.

morn-ing We shall see the Lord of Har-vest by and by.

Sunrise.

W. C. POOLE.

SOLO.

B. D. ACKLEY.

1. When I shall come to the end of my way, When I shall
2. When in His beau-ty I see the great King, Join with the
3. When life is o-ver and day-light is past, In heav-en's

rest at the close of life's day, When "Wel-come home" I shall
ran-somed His prais-es to sing, When I shall join them my
har-bor my an-chor is cast, When I see Je-sus my

hear Je-sus say, O that will be sun-rise for me..................
trib-utes to bring, O that will be sun-rise for me..................
Sav-iour at last, O that will be sun-rise for me..................

CHORUS.

Sun-rise to-mor-row, sun-rise to-mor-row, Sun-rise in glo-ry is
(Omit.................. ....

1

2

rit.

wait-ing for me; Sun-rise with Je-sus for e-ter-ni-ty.

No. 32.
Christ in the Home.

C. R. Piety.

Adam Geibel.

SOLO.

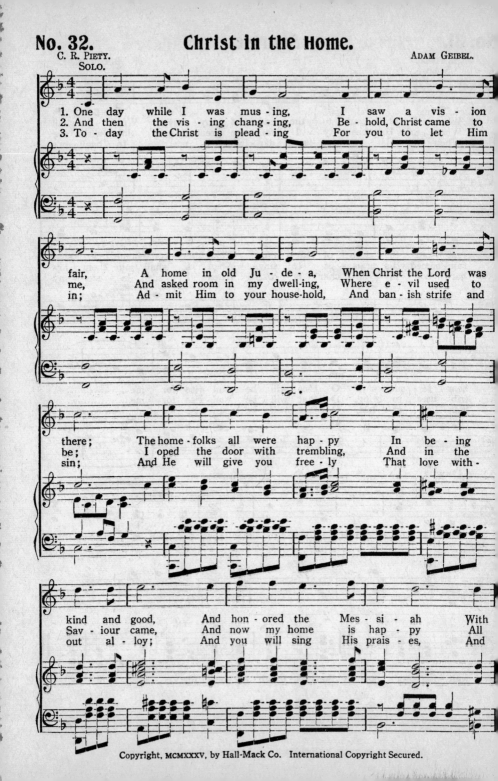

1. One day while I was mus- ing, I saw a vis- ion
2. And then the vis- ing chang- ing, Be- hold, Christ came to
3. To- day the Christ is plead- ing For you to let Him

fair, A home in old Ju - de - a, When Christ the Lord was
me, And asked room in my dwell-ing, Where e - vil used to
in; Ad - mit Him to your house-hold, And ban- ish strife and

there; The home - folks all were hap - py In be - ing
be; I oped the door with trembling, And in the
sin; And He will give you free - ly That love with-

kind and good, And hon - ored the Mes - si - ah With
Sav - iour came, And now my home is hap - py All
out al - loy; And you will sing His prais - es, And

Christ in the Home.—Concluded.

1st and 2d verses. | 3d verse.

serv - ice as they should.
praise to Je - sus' name.

serve the King for joy.

o. 33. Christ Is My Pilot.

C. Austin Miles.

Philip A. Hall.

1. Though the waves may roar and roll, 'Round my bark on life's wild sea;
2. Once the waves o-beyed His will On the sea of Gal - i - lee;
3. In His hands He keeps my life, O - ver all He will pre - vail.

I have peace with - in my soul, For the Christ will Pi - lot me.
If I trust Him and be still, He will calm the sea for me.
In the stress, the storm and strife, Christ, my Pi - lot, can - not fail.

REFRAIN.

I must not the storm be fear - ing, I must still be un - a - fraid;

p   rit.

Soon His voice I shall be hear - ing;—"It is I, be not a - fraid."

No. 34. Because He Loved Me So.

Georgie Tillman Snead.

Katherine Howe.

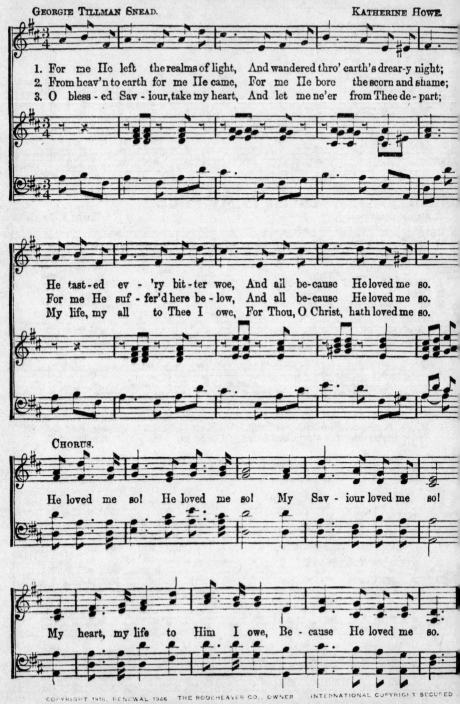

1. For me He left the realms of light, And wandered thro' earth's drear-y night;
2. From heav'n to earth for me He came, For me He bore the scorn and shame;
3. O bless-ed Sav-iour, take my heart, And let me ne'er from Thee de-part;

He tast-ed ev-'ry bit-ter woe, And all be-cause He loved me so.
For me He suf-fer'd here be-low, And all be-cause He loved me so.
My life, my all to Thee I owe, For Thou, O Christ, hath loved me so.

Chorus.

He loved me so! He loved me so! My Sav-iour loved me so!

My heart, my life to Him I owe, Be-cause He loved me so.

No. 35. The Heart that was Broken for Me.

J. W. V.

J. W. VanDeVenter.

DUET.

1. There came from the skies in the days long a-go The Lord with a
2. He came to His own— to the ones that He lov'd; The sheep that had
3. The birds have their nests, and the fox-es have holes, But He had no
4. I can-not re-ject such a Sav-iour as He; Dis-hon-or and

mes-sage of love; .... The world knew Him not, He was treated with scorn—This
wander'd a-stray; .... They heard not His voice, but the friend of mankind Was
place for His head; .... A pal-let of stone on the cold mountain side Was
wound Him a-gain; .... I'll go to His feet and re-pent of my sin, Be

CHORUS.

won-der-ful gift from a - bove. ....⎫
hat-ed and driv-en a - way. ....⎬ They crown'd Him with thorns, He was beaten with
all that He had for His bed. ....⎭
will-ing to suf-fer the pain. ... 4. I'll take up my cross, I will walk by His

stripes; He was smit-ten and nail'd to the tree, (to the tree.) But the pain in His
side, For the path-way of du-ty I see, (yes, I see,) I will fol-low my

rit.

heart was the hard-est to bear, The heart that was broken for me. .....
Lord and a-bide in His heart, The heart that was broken for me. .....

for me.

No. 36.   Consolation.

C. Austin Miles.

F. Mendelssohn.
(Arr. by Alfred Judson.)

1. Je - sus, to Thee, I kneel in sweet sub - mis - sion And own Thy bonds in
2. I did not see Thee on the cross for - sak - en, Nor yet be - hold Th
3. Not tomb, nor cross where on Thy Son was smit - ten, Forms of my life, O

D.C.—Nor would I ask for world-ly wealth or sta - tion, If I for them, mu

FINE.

rich hu - mil - i - ty; I would not know aught save my sins' re - mis - sion
from the tomb set free, But I be - lieve, nor shall my faith be shak - en,
God, the great - er part; This is my pray'r: That His name be found writ - ten,

lose my faith in Thee.

REFRAIN. Unison.

Which I re-ceived when Thou didst die for me.
For I have heard Thy kind voice call - ing me. } This do I know m
When life shall end, up - on my pulse-less heart.

great - est con - so - la - tion Comes when I kneel at Thy cross in con - te

rit.   D.

pla - tion, O Christ of Cal - va - ry! Inst.

No. 37. My Wonderful Lord.

MABEL M. STURGIS.　　　　　　　　　　　　　　　MAYBELLE KNOTT.

1. Who bore a cross up-on Cal - va-ry's hill? Je-sus, my won-der-ful Lord;
2. Who gave His life, for our sins to a - tone? Je-sus, my won-der-ful Lord;

my Lord,

Who suffered death there, His word to ful - fill? Je - sus, my won-der-ful Lord.
Who rose tri-umph-ant, to reign on a throne? Je - sus, my won-der-ful Lord.

CHORUS. Parts.

{ O hear the won - drous sto - ry, Of Christ who lives in glo - ry;
{ He suf - fered, meek and low - ly, He died to make us ho - ly;

1
He triumphed o - ver the world one day, And to heav-en He led the way.

2
Did it all to prove His un - dy - ing love, Je - sus my won-der-ful Lord.

No. 38. Will You Ask Him to Live With You?

LIZZIE DEARMOND.   D. M. SHANKS.

1. I dream'd that a stran-ger once came to my door, And He wait-ed my
2. I felt at a glance He would be my friend, That my life would be
3. Let Je-sus be Guest in your home to - day, Just to know Him will

guest to be, A won-der-ful look on His face He wore, Of com-
full of cheer, The vis - it be - gan, nev - er - more to end, For the
be to live. A soul full of song will be yours al - way, That the

pas - sion and love for me.
Christ is my com - rade dear. } O won-der-ful dream, O beau - ti - ful
Sav - iour a - lone can give.

CHORUS.

dream, That ev - 'ry one can make true, He is liv - ing with

me, my Sav - iour is He, Will you ask Him to live with you?

There Was No Room.

(*Dedicated to Dr. and Mrs. J. Gardner Clark.*)

C. A. M.

C. AUSTIN MILES.

1. When Je - sus came to earth from heav'n a bove To bring to sin - ful man re -
2. His voice could speak new life un - to the dead, Yet He had not the where to
3. In ev - 'ry heart He seeks a dwell-ing place, To ev - 'ry soul He of - fers

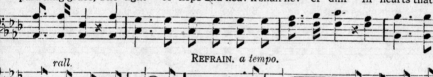

deem- ing love; He found His rest in gar-den shad-ows dim Whose ol - ive
lay His head; His bod - y lay with - in a borrowed tomb, For no - where
pard'ning grace, The light of hope and heav'n shall nev - er dim In hearts that

rall.

REFRAIN. *a tempo.*

trees made room for Him.
else was there found room.
will make room for Him.

There was no room,.............. there was no

There was no room,

rit. *a tempo.*

room,.............. No room for Je - sus in this world of sin; But there is

there was no room,

rall.

room............ with - in my heart for Thee, Lord Je - sus, come in, come in.

But there is room

come in, come in, come in.

come in.

No. 40. Above the Bright Blue.

C. E. P. Alt.

CHAS. EDW. POLLOCK.

1. There's a beau - ti - ful place call'd heav - en, It is hid - den a-
2. This land of sweet rest a - waits us, Some day it will
3. When He left His be - lov'd dis - ci - ples, He said, as He
4. We know not when He shall call us, Wheth-er soon, the glad

bove the bright blue, Where the good, who from earth-ties are riv - en,
break on our view, 'Tis prom-ised by Christ the Re - deem - er,
bade them a - dieu, "I go to pre - pare you a man - sion,
sum-mons shall be, But we know, when we pass o'er the riv - er,

CHORUS.

Live and love an e - ter - ni - ty thro'.
To His fol - low - ers faith - ful and true.
And soon I'll be send - ing for you."
The glo - ry of Je - sus we'll see.

A - bove the bright blue, th

beau - ti - ful blue, Je - sus is wait-ing for me and for you;

Heav - en is there, not far from our sight, Beau - ti - ful cit - y of light.

No. 41. How I Love the Old Hymns.

Atlanta Constitution.   M. H. EVANS.

SOLO OR DUET.

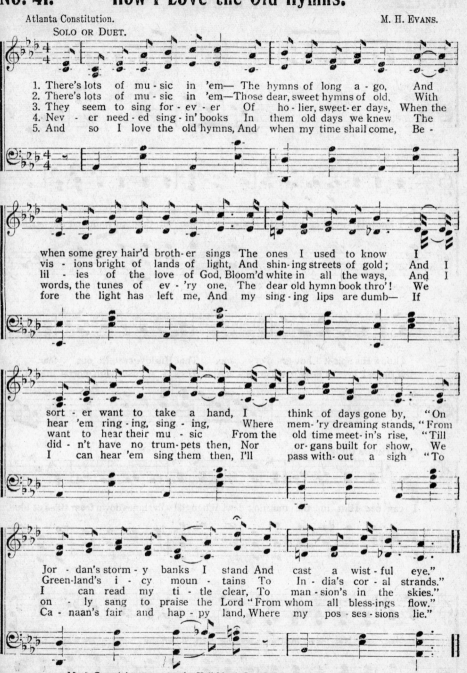

1. There's lots of mu-sic in 'em— The hymns of long a-go, And
2. There's lots of mu-sic in 'em—Those dear, sweet hymns of old, With
3. They seem to sing for-ev-er Of ho-lier, sweet-er days, When the
4. Nev-er need-ed sing-in' books In them old days we knew The
5. And so I love the old hymns, And when my time shall come, Be-

when some grey hair'd broth-er sings The ones I used to know   I
vis-ions bright of lands of light, And shin-ing streets of gold; And I
lil-ies of the love of God, Bloom'd white in all the ways, And I
words, the tunes of ev-'ry one, The dear old hymn book thro'! We
fore the light has left me, And my sing-ing lips are dumb— If

sort-er want to take a hand, I think of days gone by, "On
hear 'em ring-ing, sing-ing, Where mem-'ry dreaming stands, "From
want to hear their mu-sic From the old time meet-in's rise, "Till
did-n't have no trum-pets then, Nor or-gans built for show, We
I can hear 'em sing them then, I'll pass with-out a sigh "To

Jor-dan's storm-y banks I stand And cast a wist-ful eye."
Green-land's i-cy moun-tains To In-dia's cor-al strands."
I can read my ti-tle clear, To man-sion's in the skies."
on-ly sang to praise the Lord "From whom all bless-ings flow."
Ca-naan's fair and hap-py land, Where my pos-ses-sions lie."

NOTE:—This should not be sung in strict time. Study each verse and adapt music to words. Choruses may be sung between verses; e. g., "There'll be No Sorrow There;" "Sweet By and By;" "When the Roll is Called;" "Glory Song," etc.

No. 42.   I Know.

H. W. D.

HARRY W. DALLAS.

mf

Solo. *mf*

1. I can-not tell what lies be - fore me, I know my Fa-ther watches near.
2. I know His word is true, He keeps me, Thro' all the tu-mult and the strife,

I know His Spir-it hov-ers o'er me, That His love casteth out fear.
And those I love in heav'n will greet me, When I am done with mortal life.

QUARTET OR CHORUS.

I can see Him in the morning dew, When the sun shines down from skies of blue.

I can see His love in the wav-ing corn, When the night gives way to the

I Know.—Concluded.

No. 43. Where He Leads Me.

No. 44.

To Do His Will.

C. Austin Miles.　　　　　　　　　　　　　　　　　　M. Isabelle Ritter.

Unison.

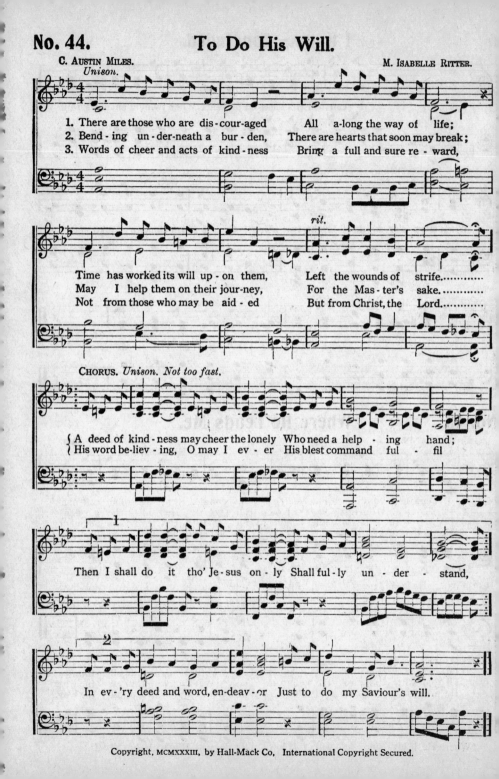

1. There are those who are dis-cour-aged　All a-long the way of life;
2. Bend-ing un-der-neath a bur-den,　There are hearts that soon may break;
3. Words of cheer and acts of kind-ness　Bring a full and sure re-ward,

rit.

Time has worked its will up-on them,　Left the wounds of strife.........
May I help them on their jour-ney,　For the Mas-ter's sake.........
Not from those who may be aid-ed　But from Christ, the Lord.........

CHORUS. *Unison. Not too fast.*

A deed of kind-ness may cheer the lonely Who need a help-ing hand;
His word be-liev-ing, O may I ev-er His blest command ful-fil

1

Then I shall do it tho' Je-sus on-ly Shall ful-ly un-der-stand,

2

In ev-'ry deed and word, en-deav-or Just to do my Saviour's will.

What Will it Matter Then?

L. S. L.

LIDA SHIVERS LEECH.

With expression.

1. Tho' I may not un-der-stand it   Why a-cross my path-way here, Come the
2. Tho' the sky is sometimes darkened, And the sun obscured from view; Still a-
3. Oft the things which most I cov-et, Are de-nied, I know not why; But I

things which most perplex me   Oft-en caus-ing doubt and fear; Still I know if I keep
bove is light and glo-ry,   Which awaits the pure and true; Just a few more days of
know I'll un-der-stand it,   When I see the King on high; In that land of un-told

stead-y, Holding fast to Je-sus' hand; None of these things here will mat-ter,
serv-ice, In the vineyard of the King; Then all care will be for-got-ten,
beau-ty, Tears will nev-er dim the eye; So I'll trust Him and be faith-ful,

CHORUS.

When I reach the glo-ry-land.   }
As to Him our sheaves we bring. } What will it matter then, What is, or might have
'Twill be bet-ter by and by.   }

rit.

been, When the gates un-fold and we en-ter in, What will it mat-ter then?

No. 46. In the Upper Garden.

C. A. M.

C. Austin Miles.

1. Just be-yond the riv-er Jor-dan   Just a-cross its chill-ing tide,
2. Grow-ing in the Up-per Gar-den,   "Flow'rs the earth too rude-ly pressed,"
3. There the buds from earth transplanted   For our com-ing watch and wait.

There's a land of life e-ter-nal,   Thro' its vales sweet waters glide.
In that land shall reach per-fec-tion   By the heav'nly Gard'ner dressed,
In that Up-per Garden grow-ing,   Just with-in the golden gate.

Girls.

By the crystal riv-er flow-ing   Grows the tree of life so fair, ..
There the flowers bloom for-ev-er,   Death can find no entrance there;
Tho' our hearts may break with sorrow,   By the grief so hard to bear,

Ma-ny loved ones wait our com-ing   In the Up-per Gar-den there.
There is life and light e-ter-nal,   There is joy be-yond com-pare.
We shall meet them some glad morning   In the Up-per Gar-den there.

CHORUS.

We shall meet them some bright morn-ing,
We shall meet them some bright morn-ing, some bright morn-ing,

In the Upper Garden.—Concluded.

Rest - ing by the wa-ters fair; . . . . . They are wait-ing for our
Rest-ing by the wa-ters fair, the wa-ters fair; They are wait - ing for our

com - ing In the Up-per Gar-den there.
com - ing, for our com-ing, In the Up-per Gar - den, in the Up-per Gar-den there.
Gar - den there.

No. 47.   Near When We Need Him.

ELSIE DUNCAN YALE.   Arr. from E. H. LEMARE.

1. Near when we need Him! Our Mas-ter, Sav-iour, Lord! "Lo, I am
2. Near when we need Him! His cour-age to im-part, "Fear not," He
3. Near when we need Him! Each day that need we know! In-to His

with you." Was ev - er sweet-er word? He gives the glo-ry Earth's
whis-pers, To ev-'ry trou-bled heart. Might-y of old-en, He
like-ness Our striv-ing souls would grow. Fain would we fol-low The

shad-ows ne'er de-stroy, Near when we need Him, His pres-ence gives joy!
bade wild bil - lows cease, Near when we need Him, His pres-ence gives peace!
One who leads a-right, Near when we need Him, His pres-ence gives light!

No. 48. That the World Might Know.

M. B. J.

Mrs. MAUDE B. JACOBS.

SOLO. *Andante.*

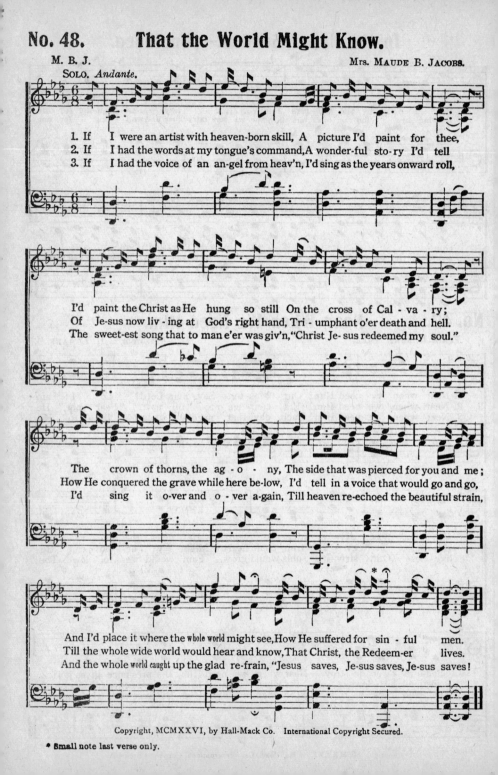

1. If I were an artist with heaven-born skill, A picture I'd paint for thee,
2. If I had the words at my tongue's command, A wonder-ful sto-ry I'd tell
3. If I had the voice of an an-gel from heav'n, I'd sing as the years onward roll,

I'd paint the Christ as He hung so still On the cross of Cal-va-ry;
Of Je-sus now liv-ing at God's right hand, Tri-umphant o'er death and hell.
The sweet-est song that to man e'er was giv'n, "Christ Je-sus redeemed my soul."

The crown of thorns, the ag-o-ny, The side that was pierced for you and me;
How He conquered the grave while here be-low, I'd tell in a voice that would go and go,
I'd sing it o-ver and o-ver a-gain, Till heaven re-echoed the beautiful strain,

And I'd place it where the whole world might see, How He suffered for sin-ful men.
Till the whole wide world would hear and know, That Christ, the Redeem-er lives.
And the whole world caught up the glad re-frain, "Jesus saves, Je-sus saves, Je-sus saves!

* Small note last verse only.

We Two.

Emily P. Miller.

C. Austin Miles.

Solo.

1. I can-not do it a - lone; The waves run fast and high; The fogs close chill a -
2. A coward, wayward and weak, I change with changing sky; I'm one day ea-ger and
3. I could not guide it myself, My boat on life's wild sea; There's One who sits by my

round, The light goes out in the sky. But I know we two shall win in the end,
brave, The next not car-ing to try, But I know we two shall win in the end,
side, Who pulls and steers with me, And I know we two shall safe en-ter port,

Je - sus and I, Yes, I know we two shall win in the end, Je - sus and I.
Je - sus and I, Yes, I know we two shall win in the end, Je - sus and I.
Je - sus and I, Yes, I know we two shall safe en-ter port, Je - sus and I.

No. 50. I Shall Be Satisfied.

(To my Friend, Herald Jenkins, Washington, D. C.)

LULU JOHNSTON. HAROLD AMADEUS MILLER.

1. I do not ask my way to see Sav - - iour mine;
2. So keep me ev - er near Thy side, Sav - - iour mine;

I on - ly wish my hand to be clasped in Thine.
And let me in Thy love a - bide, whol - - ly Thine.

Let me feel Thy presence near, When I fal - ter, when I fear,
Grant me here Thy sav-ing grace, And in heav'n to see Thy face,

And I shall be sat - is - fied, Sav - iour mine.
And I shall be sat - is - fied, Sav - iour (Omit.).................

mine.

Scripture Reading

"Who shall separate us from the love of Christ? shall tribulation, or distress, or persecution, or famine, or nakedness, or peril, or sword?"

"Nay, in all these things we are more than conquerors through him that loved us."

"For I am persuaded, that neither death, nor life, nor angels, nor principalities, nor powers, nor things present, nor things to come,"

"Nor height, nor depth, nor any other creature, shall be able to separate us from the love of God, which is in Christ Jesus our Lord."—*Romans viii: 35, 37, 38, 39.*

"For now we see through a glass, darkly; but then face to face : now I know in part; but then shall I know even as I am known."—*1 Cor. xiii: 12.*

"Beloved, now are we the sons of God, and it doth not yet appear what we shall be : but we know that, when he shall appear, we shall be like him ; for we shall see him as he is."—*1 John iii: 2.*

"As for me, I will behold thy face in righteousness : I shall be satisfied, when I awake, with thy likeness."—*Ps. xvii: 15.*

No. 52. I Have Been Alone With Jesus.

Words used by per.

Mrs. R. R. FORMAN.

SOLO OR UNISON.

1. I have been a-lone with Je-sus with my head up-on his breast,
2. With a trembling heart I told him while with joy I lin-gered there,
3. Shall I tell you what he told me while I still was wait-ing there?
4. Then he told me I was wel-come ev-er-more with him to stay,

For I was so ver-y wea-ry that I wait-ed there to rest.
All the bur-den of my sor-row and my heav-y weight of care,
For it took a-way my trou-bles and it took a-way my care;
And he said that he would nev-er cast his lov-ing child a-way.

I have been a-lone with Je-sus and he bade me stay a-while, And I
How the voice of Sa-tan's whisp'rings oft-en called me in-to sin, And I
O he told me how he lov'd me tho' a wayward, err-ing child, And I
"Lo!" He said "I am thy Sav-iour, as a rock I firm-ly stand—Come and

CHORUS. Harmony.

felt it ver-y pre-cious in the sunshine of his smile.
asked him if I might not stay for-ev-er there with him.
felt so ver-y hap-py as he look'd on me and smil'd.
rest beneath my shadow in this weary, thirst-y land." } I've been alone with Je-sus, My

bless-ed, blessed Je-sus, I've been alone with Je-sus, In the sunshine of his smile.

No. 53.

Blessed Thought.

R. E. N.

Roy E. Nolte.

1. O bless-ed thought! My Lord will be with me, Wher-e'er I
2. He knows the way, no path-way is un-known, That reach-es
3. No word of mine can ev-er ful-ly tell How much I

go, on land or on the sea,........ My faith-ful Guide, my Ad-vo-cate, my
from the man-ger to the throne...... To Him who trod each step that lies be
owe to Him I love so well;...... To serve Him here my joy shall ev-er

Friend............ In whom I'll trust un-to my jour-ney's end..........
tween............ There is no spot that is by Him un-seen........
be,.................. And praise Him "There" thro all e-ter-ni-ty...........

CHORUS.

{ O hear the sweet-est voice, Heard thro' the a-ges; Lo, I am
{ His word is ring-ing still From sa-cred *(Omit*................

with thee to the end. pag-es, To tell me Je-sus ev-er is my Friend.

No. 54.

He's the One.

J. B. M.

J. B. MACKAY.

1. Is there an - y one can help us, one who un - derstands our hearts, When the
2. Is there an - y one can help us, when the load is hard to bear, And we
3. Is there an - y one can help us, who can give a sin - ner peace, When his
4. Is there an - y one can help us, when the end is draw-ing near, Who will

thorns of life have pierced them till they bleed; One who sym - pa-thiz-es with us, who in
faint and fall beneath it in a - larm; Who in ten - derness will lift us, and the
heart is burden'd down with pain and woe; Who can speak the word of pardon that af -
go thro' death's dark waters by our side; Who will light the way be-fore us, and dis -

won - drous love im-parts Just the ver - y, ver - y blessing that we need?
heav - y bur - den share, And sup - port us with an ev - er - last-ing arm?
fords a sweet re - lease, And whose blood can wash and make us white as snow?
pel all doubt and fear, And will bear our spir - its safe - ly o'er the tide?

CHORUS.

Yes, there's One, on - ly One, The blessed, blessed Jesus, He's the One; When af-
Yes, there's One, on - ly One,

flictions press the soul, when waves of trouble roll, And you need a friend to help you, He's the One.

No. 55. The Old Faith.

L. S. L.

LIDA SHIVERS LEECH.

1. In these days of change and tur-moil, There is much to lead a-stray;
2. There are forms and doc-trines man-y, But in this they should a-gree;
3. I am stand-ing on the prom-ise That has stood for a-ges past;

But the faith of our fore-fa-thers, Is the faith that saves to-day.
That the hope of sins for-giv-en Is in Christ of Cal-va-ry.
And the faith that keeps me stead-y, Shall the storms of doubt out-last.

CHORUS

Yes, the old faith is good e-nough for me,
for me,
For it leads me to the

cross of Cal-va-ry;
of Cal-va-ry;
Then a-way to heights a-bove, I am

borne on wings of love, Yes, the old faith is good e-nough for me.
for me.

No. 56.

My Deliverer.

Mrs. J. I. McC.

(ROMANS 6: 14.)

Mrs. J. I. McCLELLAND.

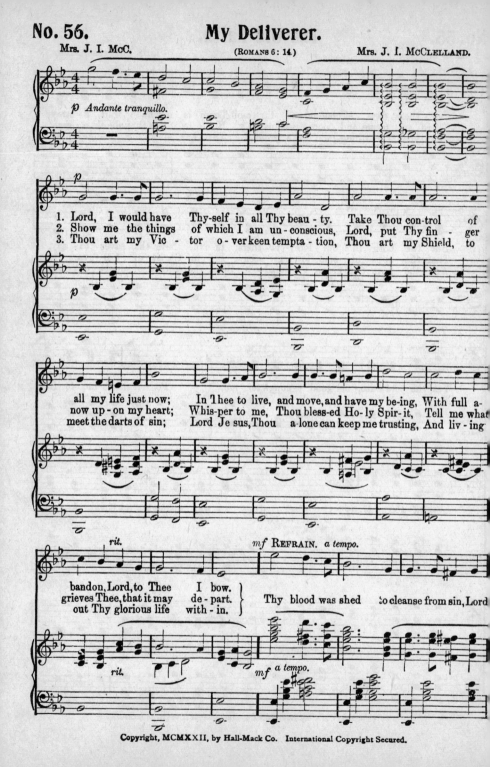

1. Lord, I would have Thy-self in all Thy beau - ty. Take Thou con-trol of
2. Show me the things of which I am un - conscious, Lord, put Thy fin - ger
3. Thou art my Vic - tor o - ver keen tempta - tion, Thou art my Shield, to

all my life just now; In Thee to live, and move, and have my be-ing, With full a-
now up - on my heart; Whis-per to me, Thou bless-ed Ho-ly Spir-it, Tell me what
meet the darts of sin; Lord Je sus, Thou a-lone can keep me trusting, And liv - ing

bandon, Lord, to Thee I bow.
grieves Thee, that it may de - part. } Thy blood was shed to cleanse from sin, Lord
out Thy glorious life with - in.

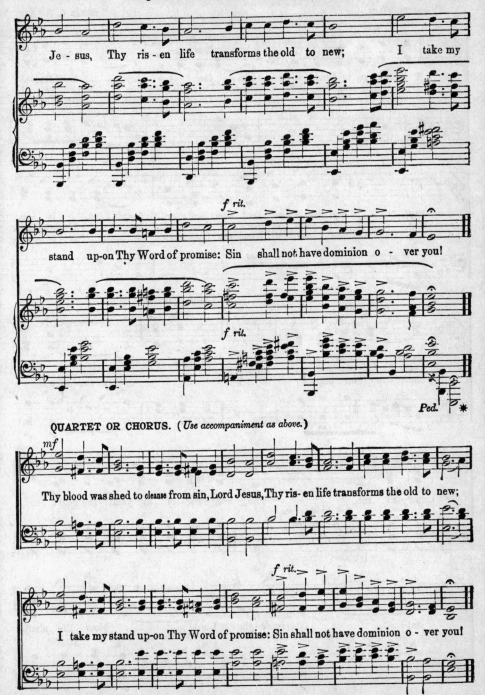

No. 58.

One Happy Day.

C. Austin Miles.
DUET.

Philip A. Hall.

1. I sought to find my heart's de - sire, One hap-py day,........... one bless-ed
2. His presence made a Par - a - dise That hap-py day,........... that bless-ed
3. From ev - 'ry sin I was set free One hap-py day,........... one bless-ed

day, And then my soul was set on fire,......... For Je - sus
day. This shall in truth for me suf - fice, ... I need naught
day. Now lost in Him my life shall be........... For - ev - er-

rit.

CHORUS. *a tempo.*

came......... with me to stay. ⎫
else........... to bless my way. ⎬ O love di - vine,................. that
more,........ one hap - py day. ⎭

O love di - vine,

came to me, The long - ing of my yearn - ing heart to

that came to me,

stay;................... O praise the Lord !................. Now life shall

my heart to stay; O praise the Lord!

One Happy Day.—Concluded.

be ... For - ev - er-more for me, one hap-py day. ... one hap - py day.

Now life shall be

No. 59. Crucified!

C. A. M.

C. AUSTIN MILES.

1. They nail'd my Lord up - on the tree And left Him, dy - ing there:
2. Up - on His head a crown of thorns, Up - on His heart my shame;
3. "For-give him, O for - give!" He cried, Then bow'd His sa - cred head;
4. His voice I hear, His love I know; I wor - ship at His feet;

Thro' love He suf - fered there for me; 'Twas love be - yond com - pare.
For me He prayed, for me He died, And, dy - ing, spoke my name.
O Lamb of God! My sac - ri - fice?" For me Thy blood was shed.
And kneel - ing there, at Cal - v'ry's cross, Re-demp - tion is com - plete.

CHORUS.

Cru - ci - fied! Cru - ci - fied! And nailed up - on the tree!

rit.

With pierc - ed hands and feet and side! For you!...... For me!......
For you! For me!

Copyright, MCMXXXI, by C. Austin Miles. Renewal.

My Best Friend.

Rev. CHAS. F. WEIGLE.

"Londonderry Air."
(Arr. and Harmonized by Clyde Willard.)

1. I have a Friend in whom I am con-fid - ing, His pres-ence fills my soul with joy each day;.............. A Friend in whom I have a peace a - bid-ing, Naught can my heart with fear or dread dis - may.

2. Come days of gloom, with heav-y weight of sor-row, 'Midst shad-ows deep, temp-ta-tions sharp and keen;............... This Friend so near, to-day and thro' to - mor-row, Dis-pels all fear— He ev-er stands be - tween.

3. This Friend of mine is Christ, the Rock of A - ges, I'll trust in Him while here on earth I roam;............... He'll keep me safe though fierce the tem-pest rag - es, Till comes the morn with-in my heav'nly home.

1. with joy each day;

REFRAIN.

He's my best Friend, to Him my soul is cling-ing, My Rock, my Strength, in
He's my best Friend,
My Rock, my Strength,

ev-'ry hour of need;.............. While He is near my heart is ev-er
in ev-'ry hour of need;

sing - ing,...... I have a Friend who is a friend to me in - deed.

No. 61.   Some Day He'll Make it Plain.

LIDA SHIVERS LEECH.   ADAM GEIBEL.

Solo, or all in unison.

1. I do not know why oft 'round me My hopes all shat-ter'd seem to be;
2. I can-not tell the depth of love, Which moves the Father's heart a-bove;
3. Tho' tri-als come thro' pass-ing days, My life will still be fill'd with praise;

God's perfect plan I can-not see, . . . But some day I'll un-der-stand.
My faith to test, my love to prove, . . But some day I'll un-der-stand.
For God will lead thro' darken'd ways, . . But some day I'll un-der-stand.

CHORUS.

Some day he'll make it plain to me, Some day when I his face shall see;

Some day from tears I shall be free, For some day I shall un - der - stand.

No. 62.

Some Day!

C. AUSTIN MILES.

GRACE L. HOSMER.

1. Tho' the hand of win-ter touch-es hill and
2. Tho' the things we love and cher-ish here be-

plain   And the glo-ries of the sum-mer flee a-way,   We may
low   From our ea-ger grasp may quickly slip a-way,   There are

sure-ly know they shall re-turn a-gain,   Some   day,   some
rich-er treas-ures com-ing, this we know,   Some   day,   some

day!   There is   One who holds the sea-sons in the   hol-low of His hand,
day!   There is   noth-ing real-ly lost in all of   God's cre-a-tive field,

So   we trust Him when our skies are gray;   What He   does in   love and
So   we leave it all to Him, and pray   That our hearts in   full sub-

Some Day!—Concluded.

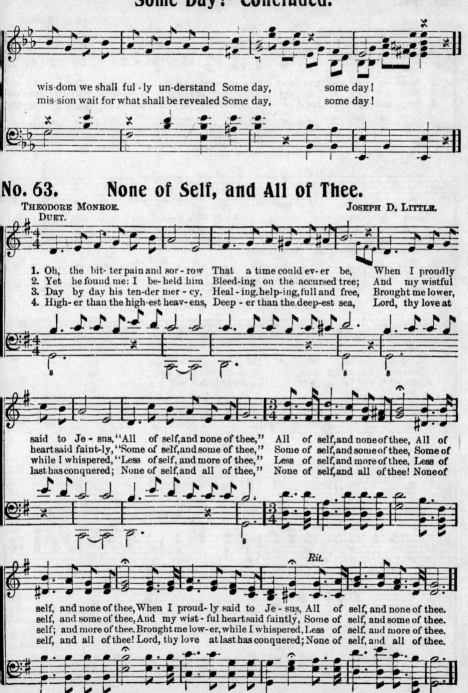

wis-dom we shall ful-ly un-derstand Some day,   some day!
mis-sion wait for what shall be revealed Some day,   some day!

No. 63. None of Self, and All of Thee.

THEODORE MONROE.
DUET.
JOSEPH D. LITTLE.

1. Oh, the bit-ter pain and sor-row That a time could ev-er be, When I proudly
2. Yet he found me: I be-held him Bleed-ing on the accursed tree; And my wistful
3. Day by day his ten-der mer-cy, Heal-ing, help-ing, full and free, Brought me lower,
4. High-er than the high-est heav-ens, Deep-er than the deep-est sea, Lord, thy love at

said to Je-sus, "All of self, and none of thee," All of self, and none of thee, All of
heart said faint-ly, "Some of self, and some of thee," Some of self, and some of thee, Some of
while I whispered, "Less of self, and more of thee," Less of self, and more of thee, Less of
last has conquered; None of self, and all of thee," None of self, and all of thee! None of

Rit.

self, and none of thee, When I proud-ly said to Je-sus, All of self, and none of thee.
self, and some of thee, And my wist-ful heart said faintly, Some of self, and some of thee.
self; and more of thee, Brought me low-er, while I whispered, Less of self, and more of thee.
self, and all of thee! Lord, thy love at last has conquered; None of self, and all of thee.

No. 64.

Back of the Clouds.

C. R. F.

CAROLYN R. FREEMAN.

DUET.—Sop. and Alto.

1. Nev-er fear tho' shad-ows dark a-round your path may fall; Do not let your
2. Win-ter long is o-ver and the spring has gone her way, Oft-en have the
3. Keep the light of hope e-ter-nal dwell-ing in your heart, Rest up-on the

heart be trou - bled; From His throne in heav-en, God is
storm-clouds gath - ered, But the rain has on-ly made the
Fa-ther's prom - ise, And you'll find that care and trou-ble

1. your heart be trou-bled;

watch-ing one and all, He will ev-er care for you...............
blos-soms look more gay, Giv-en earth a bright-er hue...............
quick-ly will de-part, Heav-en's peace will en-ter in...............

care for you.

CHORUS. *All, in Two Parts.*

Back of the clouds the sun is al-ways shin-ing, Aft-er the

(Simile.)

Four Parts.

storms your skies will all be blue; God has pre-pared a

pre-pared

Back of the Clouds.—Concluded.

ros-y-tint-ed lin-ing, Back of the clouds it's wait-ing to shine thro'.

No. 65.   The Voice of Jesus.

A. H. A.

Rev. A. H. ACKLEY.

Unison.

1. I hear a voice   so soft and low,   Its tones of love   pos- sess me,
2. I hear it in   the days of care,   When hearts and flesh   grow wea - ry,
3. I hear it in   the storm-y wind,   That bows my head   with weep-ing,
4. I hear it ev - 'rywhere I go,   And Christ His word   has giv - en,

Like some sweet song   of long a - go,   It lin-gers to   ca - ress me.
It saves my spir - it from de-spair,   And lights the way   so drear - y,
It makes me know   that God is kind,   And I am in   His keep-ing.
That same sweet voice that here I know,   Shall welcome me   to heav - en.

REFRAIN.

It falls like mu - sic on my ear,   And drives a - way   my doubt and

fear,   It is the voice   of God I hear,   The blessed voice   of Je - sus.

No. 66. By and By.

CHAS. H GABRIEL. B. D. ACKLEY.

SOLO.

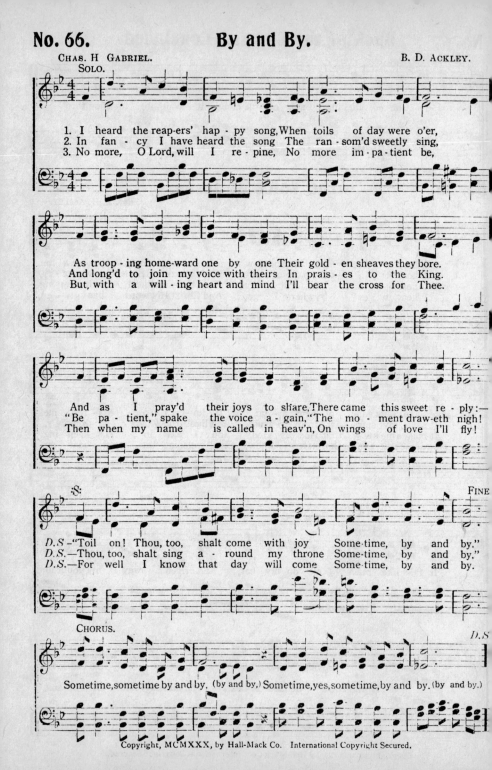

1. I heard the reap-ers' hap-py song, When toils of day were o'er,
2. In fan-cy I have heard the song The ran-som'd sweetly sing,
3. No more, O Lord, will I re-pine, No more im-pa-tient be,

As troop-ing home-ward one by one Their gold-en sheaves they bore.
And long'd to join my voice with theirs In prais-es to the King.
But, with a will-ing heart and mind I'll bear the cross for Thee.

And as I pray'd their joys to share, There came this sweet re-ply:—
"Be pa-tient," spake the voice a-gain, "The mo-ment draw-eth nigh!
Then when my name is called in heav'n, On wings of love I'll fly!

FINE

D.S—"Toil on! Thou, too, shalt come with joy Some-time, by and by."
D.S.—Thou, too, shalt sing a-round my throne Some-time, by and by."
D.S.—For well I know that day will come Some-time, by and by.

CHORUS.

D.S

Sometime, sometime by and by, (by and by,) Sometime, yes, sometime, by and by. (by and by.)

No. 67.   God Forgot All My Sins.

MAUD FRAZER JACKSON.   C. AUSTIN MILES.

1. I would sing of the grace that met me   When I came up to Cal - va - ry;
2. Long the bur-den of sin I car-ried,   Till to Je-sus for help I cried;
3. I'm no more beneath con-dem-na-tion,   Re-con-ciled un-to God at last;
4. Are you yet the sin-bur-den bear-ing?   Christ has died that you might go free;

How my sins are of God for-got-ten,   Bur-ied deep-ly as in   the seal
Now I'm free who was once in bond-age,   By the blood of the Lamb who died.
And the love that has all for-giv-en,   Is the love that will hold me fast.
God will par-don you now, O sin-ner, And will love through e-ter-ni-ty.

CHORUS.

My sins are for-giv-en, for-got-ten for aye! No won-der I'm

sing-ing   for glad-ness to-day; God for-got all   my sins there at

Cal-va-ry, He for-got all   my sins, but re-mem-bers me.

No. 68. The Fruit of the Spirit.

C. AUSTIN MILES. GAL. 5: 22, 23. PHILIP A. HALL.

1. Give me no treasures that last but a while,
2. Treasures of sil-ver, of gems or of gold
3. Pa-tience and love, and a life that shall be

But, Lord, I pray, show me each day Some one whose load I may
Last but a day, they slip a-way; But there are treas-ures I
Like un-to Thine, Sav-iour di-vine; Give of the fruit of the

CHORUS.

lift with a smile, Some one who's go-ing my way.
sure-ly may hold; Give them to me, Lord, I pray.
Spir-it to me; Then shall I say, "This is *mine!*"

Noth-ing is mine if I

must leave it here, When I have end-ed my earth-ly ca-reer.

The Fruit of the Spirit.—Concluded.

Filled with the fruit of the Spir-it di-vine, "This," I shall say, "is mine!"......

No. 69. Up Calvary's Hill.

C. Austin Miles.
DUET. *Slowly.*

Clarence Kohlmann.

1. Up Calv'ry's hill Je-sus pa-tient-ly trod, Yielding His will to the will of His God.
2. That crown He wears still in visions I see, That cross He bears, He is bear-ing for me.
3. "Father, forgive!" He is pray-ing for me; "Lord, while I live let me not forget Thee!"

CHORUS.

Par-doned, it shall suf-fice; Pur-chased— O what a price Je-sus paid for
me,...... There on Cal-va-ry...... Suf-f'ring, He bore my shame,
for me...... There on........... Cal-va-ry.
Dy-ing, He spoke my name; Lov-ing, liv-ing, dy-ing, giv-ing All for me.

No. 70. He'll Drive All the Shadows Away.

C. C. UHLAND.   ADAM GEIBEL.

SOLO, or all in Unison.

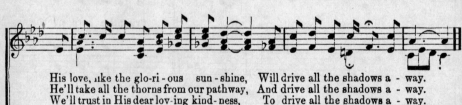

1. The cares of the day oft per-plex us,   The pathway we tread oft seems bare,
2. That life which the sun never brightened,   With mis-ery and pain ev'ry-where.
3. There's no one can help us like Je-sus,   No burden's too heav-y for Him,

The sun seems to shine but for oth-ers;   There seems to be no one to   care,
May reach out in faith and may find Him   Who waits ev-'ry sor-row to   share.
He wants ev'ry life filled with sunshine;   With light that shall never grow dim,

But some one is watching our foot-steps,   He's guid-ing us o'er the dark   way;
He holds out His hands pierc'd and wounded,   He knows of the bur-den each   day;
And dai-ly He's watching our footsteps,   And lead-ing us all the lone   way;

His love, like the glo-ri-ous sun-shine,   Will drive all the shadows a - way.
He'll take all the thorns from our pathway,   And drive all the shadows a - way.
We'll trust in His dear lov-ing kind-ness,   To drive all the shadows a - way.

No. 71. Some Glad, Sweet Day.

H. L.

HALDOR LILLENAS.

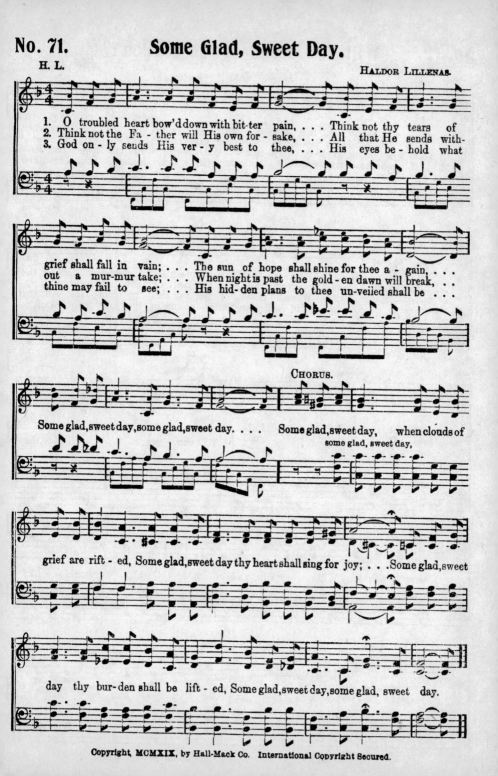

1. O troubled heart bow'd down with bit-ter pain, ... Think not thy tears of
2. Think not the Fa - ther will His own for - sake, ... All that He sends with-
3. God on - ly sends His ver - y best to thee, ... His eyes be - hold what

grief shall fall in vain; ... The sun of hope shall shine for thee a - gain, ...
out a mur-mur take; ... When night is past the gold - en dawn will break, ...
thine may fail to see; ... His hid - den plans to thee un-veiled shall be ...

CHORUS.

Some glad, sweet day, some glad, sweet day. ... Some glad, sweet day, when clouds of
some glad, sweet day,

grief are rift - ed, Some glad, sweet day thy heart shall sing for joy; ... Some glad, sweet

day thy bur-den shall be lift - ed, Some glad, sweet day, some glad, sweet day.

No. 72.   Will You Stand in the Garden?

JENNIE E. HUSSEY.   C. AUSTIN MILES.

1. Will you stand in the gar-den with Je-sus? Will you own Him when
2. Will you stand in Geth-sem-a-ne's gar-den, With the Sav-iour who
3. There's a bright, gold-en day for whose dawn-ing All His loved and His
4. If you stood with your Lord in the gar-den, And up-held Him when

oth-ers de-ny? When the world waits to mock Him and scourge Him, Or the
suf-fered for you? Will you rise in the hall of the judg-ment And up-
own watch and pray, When in clouds of the sky He'll be com-ing, And that
oth-ers de-nied, He will men-tion your name in the judg-ment, Grant a

CHORUS.

throngs of the care-less go by?
hold Him with loy-al-ty true?
day, O it may be to day.
crown and a throne at His side.

Will you stand............... in the
Will you stand

gar-den with Him? Will you own Him while others de-ny? Or would you, like

rall.

Ju-das, be-tray with a kiss, And let Him go out to die?

Copyright, MCMXXVII, by Hall-Mack Co.   International Copyright Secured.

No. 73.   All Life's Way.

VALERIA R. LEHMAN.   M. ISABELLE RITTER.

SOP. AND ALTO, OR UNISON.

1. Not just in mo-ments of doubt or sad-ness, With me, dear Sav-iour,
2. In life's sweet springtime, when days go wing-ing, Help me to walk in
3. Thy life of beau-ty is bright be-fore me, To lead me ev-er

would I have Thee stay; Nor on-ly mo-ments of joy or glad-ness,
wis-dom by Thy side; When age comes creep-ing, more close-ly cling-ing,
on to heights a-bove; Thy hands in bless-ing are lift-ed o'er me,

CHORUS.

I need Thee, Mas-ter, all the way..........⎫
I pray Thee, Lord, with me a-bide.........⎬ I need Thee, Je-sus, thro' ev-'ry
To keep me safe-ly in Thy love..........⎭

mo-ment, I need Thy guid-ance a-mid the fray; To-day, to-

mor-row, in joy or sor-row, I need Thee, Sav-iour, all life's way.

No. 74. The Everlasting Love.

W. C. POOLE. C. AUSTIN MILES.

UNISON.

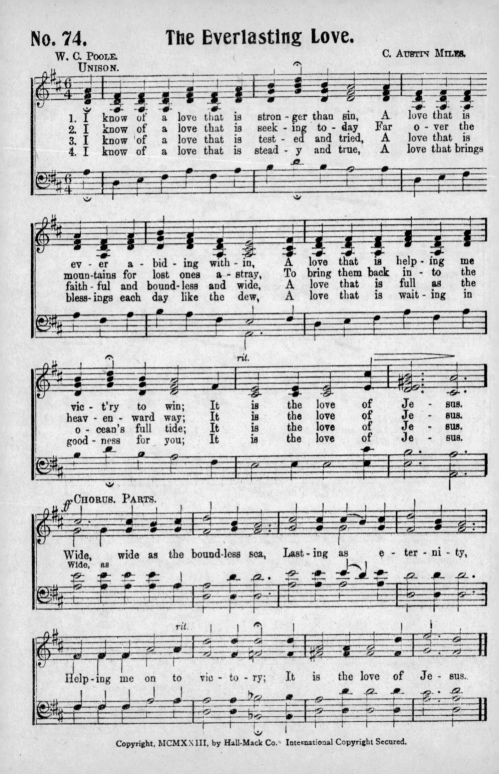

1. I know of a love that is stron-ger than sin, A love that is
2. I know of a love that is seek-ing to-day Far o-ver the
3. I know of a love that is test-ed and tried, A love that is
4. I know of a love that is stead-y and true, A love that brings

ev-er a-bid-ing with-in, A love that is help-ing me
moun-tains for lost ones a-stray, To bring them back in-to the
faith-ful and bound-less and wide, A love that is full as the
bless-ings each day like the dew, A love that is wait-ing in

rit.

vic-t'ry to win; It is the love of Je - sus.
heav-en-ward way; It is the love of Je - sus.
o-cean's full tide; It is the love of Je - sus.
good-ness for you; It is the love of Je - sus.

CHORUS. PARTS.

Wide, wide as the bound-less sea, Last-ing as e-ter-ni-ty,
Wide, as

rit.

Help-ing me on to vic-to-ry; It is the love of Je-sus.

No. 75. All Alone.

C. A. M.

C. AUSTIN MILES.

1. Have you ev - er tried to bear your bur - dens All a - lone? All a-
2. Don't you know He "trod the wine-press for you All a - lone? All a-
3. Don't you know that He has bought your par - don All a - lone? All a-

All a-lone?

lone? Don't you know there's One who waits to help you, Who will make all your
lone? And the bur - den that He bore in meek-ness, Such a bur - den no
lone? And your grat - i - tude for such a mer - cy Un - to Je - sus you

CHORUS.

bur - dens His own?)
oth - er has known. } When I have bur-dens to bear which no one can share, I
nev - er have shown.)

take them to Je - sus the Man of Cal - va - ry; When I have cross-es to bear, my

Sav-iour is there, And al-ways takes the heav-y end, and gives the light to me.

No. 76.   He Loves Me, More Than I Can Tell.

Rev. Alfred Barratt.

John J. Thomas.

Intro.

Solo or Unison.

1. In sorrow's night the Saviour found me, He broke the chains of sin that bound me,
2. I cannot stray while He is guiding; While in His love my soul is hid - ing;
3. His love for me is still un-ceas-ing, His grace is ev-er-more in-creas-ing,
4. When day is done and night is nearing, And when the light is dis-ap-pear-ing,

He threw His arms of love a-round me; He loves me, more than I can tell.
With - in my heart He is a - bid - ing; He loves me, more than I can tell.
His ten - der care is nev - er ceas - ing; He loves me, more than I can tell.
This thought my heart shall still be cheering, He loves me, more than I can tell.

Refrain. *Parts.*

He loves me, more than I can tell, I know He loves me O so well;

can tell,

In weal or woe, and wher-e'er I go He loves me, more than I can tell.

No. 77. Submission.

C. AUSTIN MILES.   Mrs. R. R. FORMAN.

1. The path that I have trod, Has bro't me nearer God, Tho' oft it
2. The cross that I must bear, If I a crown would wear, Is not the
3. Submission to the will Of Him who guides me still Is surety

led........ thro' sorow's gates. Tho' not the way I'd choose, In my way I might lose
cross..... that I should take; But, since on me 'tis laid, I'll take it, un-a-fraid,
of......... His love revealed; My soul shall rise a-bove This world in which I move;

REFRAIN.

The joy that yet for me a-waits.
And bear it for the Mas-ter's sake. } Not what I wish to be, Nor where I
I con-quer on-ly where I yield.

wish to go, For who am I that I should choose my way? The Lord shall

choose for me, 'Tis bet-ter far, I know, So let Him bid me go, or stay.

No. 78. My Jesus, I Love Thee.

London Hymn Book.

Slow, with expression.

J. L. GILBERT.

1. My Je-sus, I love Thee, I know Thou art mine; For Thee all the fol-lies of
2. I'll love Thee in life, I will love Thee in death, And praise Thee as long as Thou

sin I re-sign; My gra-cious Re-deem-er, my Sav-iour art Thou; If
lend-est me breath; And say when the death-dew lies cold on my brow: "If

A little faster.

ev-er I loved Thee, my Je-sus, 'tis now. I love Thee be-cause Thou hast
ev-er I loved Thee, my Je-sus, 'tis now." In man-sions of glo-ry and

slower.

first lov-ed me, And purchas'd my par-don on Cal-va-ry's tree; I love Thee for
end-less de-light, I'll ev-er a-dore Thee in heav-en so bright; I'll sing with the

pp

wear-ing the thorns on Thy brow, If ev-er I loved Thee, my Je-sus 'tis now.
glit-ter-ing crown on my brow: "If ev-er I loved Thee, my Je-sus 'tis now."

But This I Know.

C. Austin Miles.   *(Dedicated to Gipsy Smith.)*   Clarence Kohlmann.

1. I do not know the depths of Je - sus' love, That bro't Him down to earth
2. I do not know what pain He suf-fered there, The bur - den of my sin
3. I do not know what I can do, or say, My debt of grat - i - tude

from heav'n a - bove, Nor why He bore the cross up Cal - va - ry And shed His
and shame to bear. It may be well to hide it all from me, Lest my own
to Him I pay; But I at least may cry, "O Christ di - vine! Had I a

Refrain.

pre-cious blood so will - ing - ly.
heart should break in sym - pa - thy. } But this one thing I know; That, when the
thou-sand lives they should be Thine."

crim - son flow Dropped to the earth be - low, it fell on me. My eyes were

rit.

opened wide, I saw Him cru - ci - fied, And knew for me He died on Cal- va - ry.

No. 80.

O Dawn Supreme!

JAMES ROWE.

B. D. ACKLEY.

1. O dawn su - preme,............. when I shall rise, To meet my
2. O dawn su - preme,............. when, tri - als past, I shall be
3. O morn su - preme,............. when with the throng I shall up

Lord in Par - a - dise; To live with Him......... on that fair shore,
safe at home at last, No more to walk........ these thorn-y ways,
lift my voice in song, In praise of Him........ whose love will be

And share His love........... for - ev - er- more!
But to re - joice......... thro' countless days!
The theme for all............ e - ter - ni - ty!

CHORUS.

O dawn supreme! O
O dawn, O dawn supreme! O

morn of bliss, When I shall place my hand in His
morn, O morn of bliss, my hand in His

O Dawn Supreme!—Concluded.

And, in the glo-ry of His face, Ex-tol Him for re-deem-ing grace!

No. 81. My Saviour's Love For Me.

WILLIAM C. POOLE.

C. AUSTIN MILES.

1. See - ing me far from the path-way a - stray, Com-ing to show me the
2. Liv - ing, He showed me His life with - out sin; Sav - ing me, helped me new
3. Pray - ing, He taught me the pow - er of pray'r, Liv - ing, He showed me to
4. Wear-ing the thorn crown, O how could it be? Bear-ing the cross load up

heavenward way, Je-sus, my Saviour came seeking one day, Seeking (for me,) for me.
life to be - gin, Giv-ing me pow - er the vic-t'ry to win, Liv-ing (for me,) for me.
love and to care; Out in the gar-den, I think of Him there, Praying (for me,) for me.
rough Cal-va-ry; Dy-ing for sinners, from sin to set free, Dy-ing (for me,) for me.

Chorus.

Down from the Fa-ther's throne a-bove, For me He came in won-drous love;

rit.

To Beth-le-hem and Cal - va - ry, Love led Him on— for you and me.

No. 82. He Is Coming Again.

JENNIE E. HUSSEY.

C. AUSTIN MILES.

1. When the Sav-iour had gone in-to heav-en, And a cloud had re-
2. "This same Je-sus, now gone in-to heav-en, In like man-ner shall
3. He is com-ing a-gain as He prom-ised, When the war-clouds have

ceived Him from sight; Watching an-gels fore-told His dis-ci-ples, That a-
so come a-gain;" And your eyes shall be-hold Him in glo-ry, For His
all rolled a-way; And His beau-ti-ful feet on the mount-ains Shall be-

CHORUS.

gain they should see Him in light.)
kingdom shall rule o-ver men. } He is com-ing a-gain, O be-lieve it,
tok-en the dawn-ing of day.)

His prom-ise is true, then re-ceive it; He is com-ing for you,

He is com-ing for me, He is com-ing to gath-er His own. . . . . .
gath-er His own.

No. 83.

Like Jesus.

(To my Friend, LeRoy E. Froom.)

A. D. ELLINGTON.—Chorus added.

HAROLD A. MILLER.

Prayerfully. (Play four measures for Intro.)

1. Teach me, Fa-ther, what to say; Teach me, Father, how to pray; Teach me all a-
2. Teach me as the days go by, Teach me not to rea-son why, Teach me that to
3. Teach me that the time is short, Teach me how to live and work, Teach me that to
4. Teach me how we may be one, Like the Fa-ther and the Son; And when all is

rit.　CHORUS. *mf*

long the way, How to be like Je - sus.
do and die, Is to be like Je - sus.
nev - er shirk Is to be like Je - sus.
o - ver-come, I will be like Je - sus.

I would be like Je - sus, I would

rit.　*mf*

cres.　*rit.*　*rit.*

be like Je - sus! Help me Lord, to dai - ly grow　More and more like Je - sus!

cres.　*rit.*　*rit.*

No. 84. To See Thy Face.

(Inscribed to my friend, Horace Shaw, Washington Missionary College.)

ETHEL HOSKING.   HAROLD AMADEUS MILLER.

Moderato.

BARITONE SOLO. *a tempo.*

1. Sav - iour di - vine, my heart is filled with long - ing For that glad day when
2. But now in mer - cy Thou dost hide Thy glo - ry, While I, thro' faith, can
3. Some day the plan di - vine, which now per - plex - es, Ah, let me see and

Melody.

rall. *cres.*

I shall see Thy face, And all these pains and doubts and fears forget - ting,
feel Thy guiding hand, And trust Thy wis - dom, for I know these tri - als
kiss those hands, nail riv'n, And I'll re - mem - ber thro' th'e - ter - nal a - ges,

rall. f *rit. e dim.* REFRAIN. *Longingly.*

Shall un - der - stand the wonders of Thy grace.
Shall blessings prove, ah, let me un - der - stand.   To see Thy face!
Thy life, dear Lord, for my poor life was giv'n.

rit. f *rit.*

To see Thy face! Some day, not dis - tant, Lord, I'll see Thy face!

Nothing New to Me.

H. L.

HALDOR LILLENAS.

1. To hold communion with the Lord,......... Is noth-ing new,...... is noth-ing
2. To have Him lift my load of care,......... Is noth-ing new,...... is noth-ing
3. To hear the mu-sic of His voice,....... Is noth-ing new,...... is noth-ing
4. To have the world grow strangely dim,........ Is noth-ing new,...... is noth-ing

new;........ To feed up-on His sa-cred word........ Is noth-ing
new;........ To have His an-swer to my pray'r........ Is noth-ing
new;........ To make His sov'reign will my choice..... Is noth-ing
new;........ Be-cause ot light that shines from Him......... Is noth-ing

new to me; To feel His gracious guiding hand,...... And
new to me; To be my Friend when others fail,........ To
new to me; To trust in Him when skies are drear,...... To
new to me, To yield my all to His con-trol,..... ..... My

on His promise firm-ly stand, To walk with Him in Beu-lah land
be my strength when foes assail, To pi - lot me thro' storm and gale
yield to Him my ev-'ry fear, To have Him dry my fall-ing tear
ev-'ry bur-den on Him roll,........ To have Him live within my soul

Is noth-ing new to me,........... Is noth-ing new... to me.

No. 86. The Sacrifice.

J. M.
DUET.

JOHNSTON MORRIS.

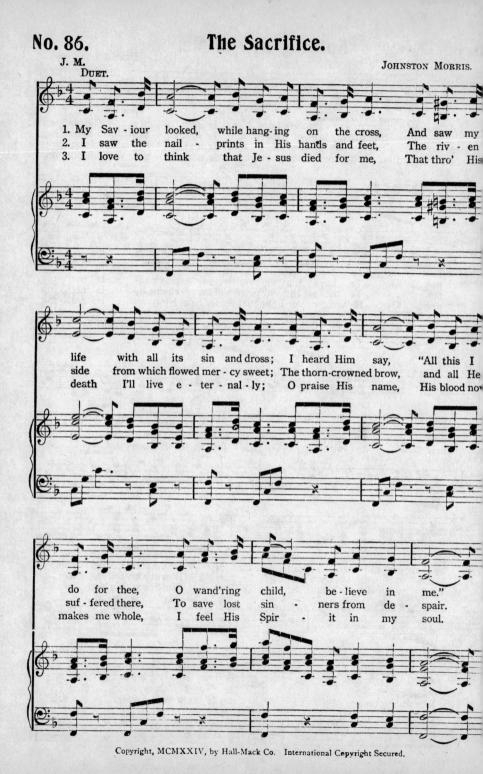

1. My Sav - iour looked, while hang-ing on the cross, And saw my
2. I saw the nail - prints in His hands and feet, The riv - en
3. I love to think that Je - sus died for me, That thro' His

life with all its sin and dross; I heard Him say, "All this I
side from which flowed mer - cy sweet; The thorn-crowned brow, and all He
death I'll live e - ter - nal - ly; O praise His name, His blood now

do for thee, O wand'ring child, be - lieve in me."
suf - fered there, To save lost sin - ners from de - spair.
makes me whole, I feel His Spir - it in my soul.

The Sacrifice.—Concluded.

REFRAIN. QUARTET.*

I love to think............ I'll see Him face, to face, And know the
I love to think

full-ness of re-deem-ing grace; I'll sing His praise............ for all His
I'll sing His praise

love for me, And serve Him through............ e-ter-ni-ty............
And serve Him thro'   e-ter-ni-ty.

* May be sung as Duet

No. 87.   I Shall Not Pass Again This Way.

Unknown.   C. Austin Miles.

1. The bread that giveth strength I want to give; The wa-ter pure that bids the thirst-y live;
2. I   want to give the oil of joy for tears; The faith to conquer cru-el doubts and fears.
3. I   want to give good measure running o'er, And in-to an-gry hearts I want to pour
4. I   want to give to others hope and faith. I want to do all that the Master saith;

Marcato.   rit.   rall.

I want to help the fainting day by day, Because I shall not pass a-gain this way.
Beauty for ash-es may I give al-way, Because I shall not pass a-gain this way.
The answer soft that turneth wrath a-way, Because I shall not pass a-gain this way.
I want to live aright from day to day, Because I shall not pass a-gain this way.

* Small notes for last verse.

No. 88.
I Do Not Ask.

C. AUSTIN MILES.
DUET OR SOLO.

ADAM GEIBEL.

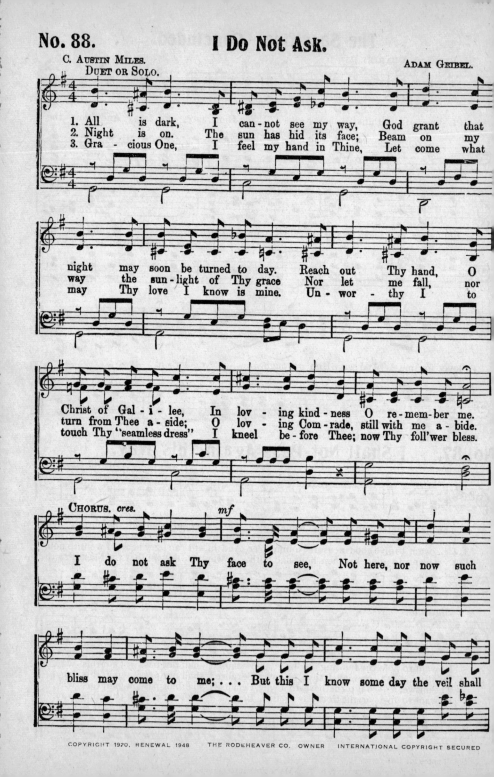

1. All is dark, I can-not see my way, God grant that
2. Night is on. The sun has hid its face; Beam on my
3. Gra - cious One, I feel my hand in Thine, Let come what

night may soon be turned to day. Reach out Thy hand, O
way the sun-light of Thy grace Nor let me fall, nor
may Thy love I know is mine. Un - wor - thy I to

Christ of Gal - i - lee, In lov - ing kind - ness O re-mem-ber me.
turn from Thee a - side; O lov - ing Com - rade, still with me a - bide.
touch Thy "seamless dress" I kneel be - fore Thee; now Thy foll'wer bless.

CHORUS. cres.   mf

I do not ask Thy face to see, Not here, nor now such

bliss may come to me; ... But this I know some day the veil shall

I Do Not Ask.—Concluded.

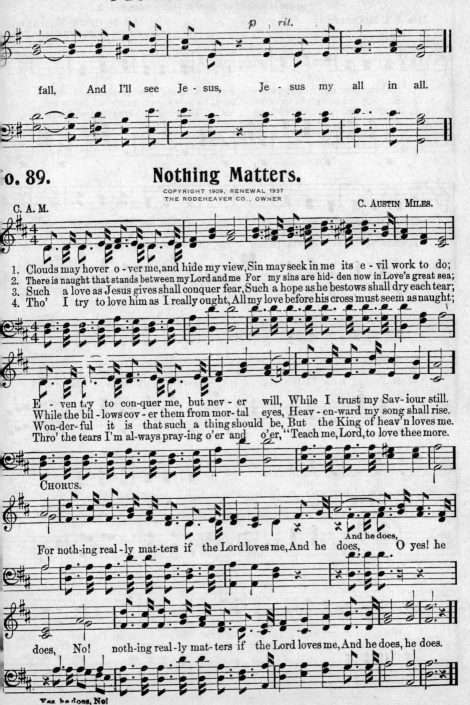

p   rit.

fall,   And   I'll   see   Je - sus,   Je - sus   my   all   in   all.

No. 89.   Nothing Matters.

C. A. M.

C. Austin Miles.

1. Clouds may hover o - ver me, and hide my view, Sin may seek in me its e - vil work to do;
2. There is naught that stands between my Lord and me For my sins are hid- den now in Love's great sea;
3. Such a love as Jesus gives shall conquer fear, Such a hope as he bestows shall dry each tear;
4. Tho' I try to love him as I really ought, All my love before his cross must seem as naught;

E - ven try to con-quer me, but nev - er will, While I trust my Sav-iour still.
While the bil - lows cov - er them from mor - tal eyes, Heav - en-ward my song shall rise.
Won-der-ful it is that such a thing should be, But the King of heav'n loves me.
Thro' the tears I'm al-ways pray-ing o'er and o'er, "Teach me, Lord, to love thee more.

Chorus.

For noth-ing real - ly mat-ters if the Lord loves me, And he does, O yes! he

And he does,

does, No! noth-ing real - ly mat-ters if the Lord loves me, And he does, he does.

Yes he does, No!

No. 90. Whispering Hope.

"We * * rejoice in hope of the glory of God."—ROMANS 5: 2.

Mrs. J. I. McCLELLAND.

Arr. by CLYDE WILLARD.
From "Whispering Hope."

DUET.

1. Like the faint dawn of the morn - ing, Like the sweet freshness of dew,
2. Sing-ing the song of for-give - ness, Soft-ly I hear in my soul,
3. Hope is an an-chor to keep us, Hold-ing both steadfast and sure;

Comes the dear whis-per of Je - sus, Com-fort-ing, ten-der and true.
Je - sus has conquered for-ev - er Sin with its fear-ful con-trol.
Hope brings a won-der-ful cleans - ing, Thro' His blood, making us pure.

Dark-ness gives way to the sun - light, While His voice falls on my ear;
Whis-per-ing cour-age for war - fare, Bend-ing Thine ear when I pray;
Whis-per-ing hope of His com - ing, How my heart thrills at His Word!

Sea-sons of heav-en's re-fresh - ing, Call to new glad-ness and cheer.
Glo - ri-ous, ris-en Re-deem - er, O how I praise Thee to-day!
O to be watching and wait - ing, Read - y to wel-come the Lord!

CHORUS.

Whis - per-ing hope,........ like the song.......... of the an - gels,
Whis - per-ing hope, whis-per-ing hope, Angel's sweet song, angel's sweet song,

Whispering Hope.—Concluded.

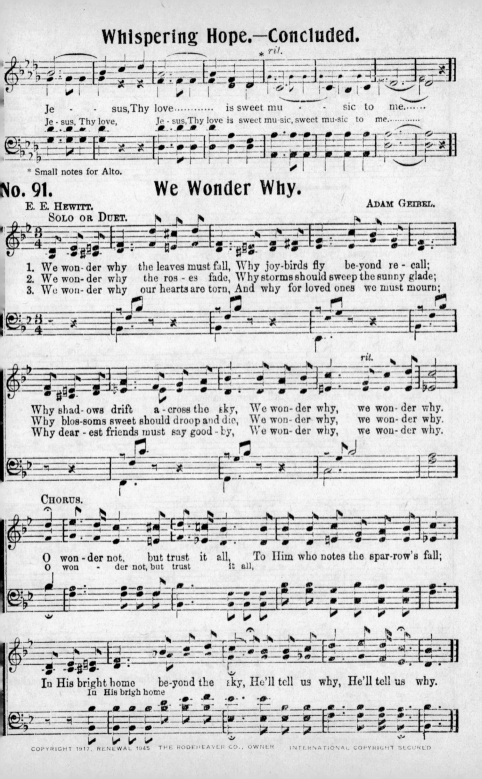

* rit.

Je - - - sus, Thy love............. is sweet mu - - - sic to me......
Je - sus, Thy love,   Je - sus, Thy love is sweet mu-sic, sweet mu-sic to me..........

* Small notes for Alto.

No. 91.   We Wonder Why.

E. E. HEWITT.

ADAM GEIBEL.

SOLO OR DUET.

1. We won- der why   the leaves must fall, Why joy-birds fly   be-yond re - call;
2. We won- der why   the ros- es   fade, Why storms should sweep the sunny glade;
3. We won- der why   our hearts are torn, And why for loved ones we must mourn;

rit.

Why shad- ows drift   a - cross the sky,   We won- der why,   we won- der why.
Why blos-soms sweet should droop and die,   We won- der why,   we won- der why.
Why dear - est friends must say good - by,   We won- der why,   we won- der why.

CHORUS.

O won- der not,   but trust it all,   To Him who notes the spar-row's fall;
O won- der not, but trust   it all,

In His bright home   be-yond the sky, He'll tell us why, He'll tell us why.
In His brigh home

No. 92.   He Always Knows.

James Rowe.   HALDOR LILLENAS.

SOP. AND ALTO.

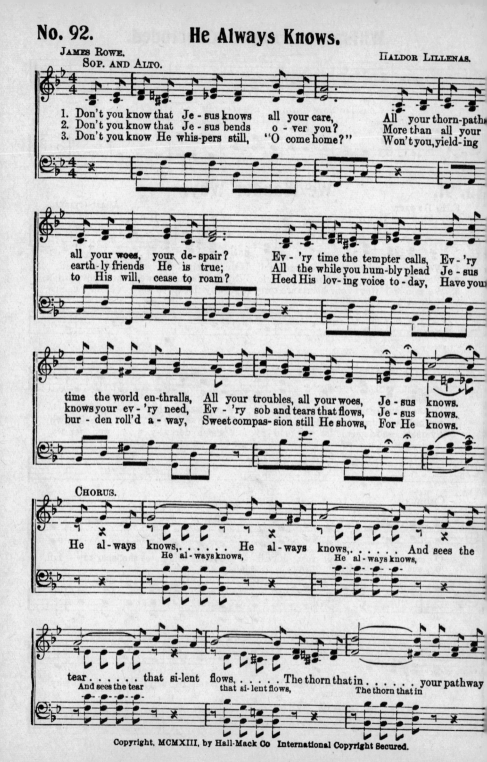

1. Don't you know that Je-sus knows   all your care,   All your thorn-path
2. Don't you know that Je-sus bends   o - ver you?   More than all your
3. Don't you know He whis-pers still, "O come home?"   Won't you, yield-ing

all your woes, your de-spair?   Ev - 'ry time the tempter calls,   Ev - 'ry
earth-ly friends He is true;   All the while you hum-bly plead   Je - sus
to His will, cease to roam?   Heed His lov-ing voice to - day,   Have your

time the world en-thralls,   All your troubles, all your woes,   Je - sus knows.
knows your ev - 'ry need,   Ev - 'ry sob and tears that flows,   Je - sus knows.
bur - den roll'd a - way,   Sweet compas- sion still He shows,   For He knows.

CHORUS.

He al - ways knows,...... He al - ways knows,...... And sees the
He al - ways knows,   He al - ways knows,

tear...... that si - lent flows,...... The thorn that in...... your pathway
And sees the tear   that si - lent flows,   The thorn that in

He Always Knows.—Concluded.

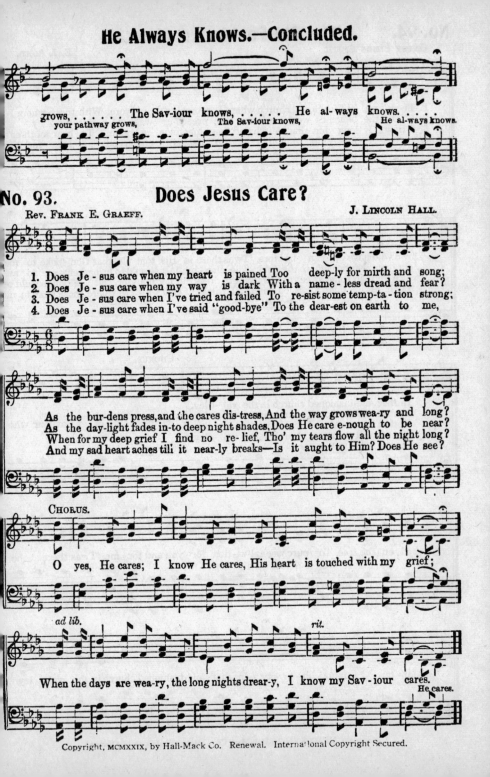

grows, ... The Sav-iour knows, ... He al-ways knows. ....
your pathway grows,   The Sav-iour knows,   He al-ways knows.

No. 93.   Does Jesus Care?

Rev. Frank E. Graeff.

J. Lincoln Hall.

1. Does Je - sus care when my heart is pained Too deep-ly for mirth and song;
2. Does Je - sus care when my way is dark With a name - less dread and fear?
3. Does Je - sus care when I've tried and failed To re-sist some temp-ta - tion strong;
4. Does Je - sus care when I've said "good-bye" To the dear-est on earth to me,

As the bur-dens press, and the cares dis-tress, And the way grows wea-ry and long?
As the day-light fades in-to deep night shades, Does He care e-nough to be near?
When for my deep grief I find no re-lief, Tho' my tears flow all the night long?
And my sad heart aches till it near-ly breaks—Is it aught to Him? Does He see?

Chorus.

O yes, He cares; I know He cares, His heart is touched with my grief;

ad lib.   *rit.*

When the days are wea-ry, the long nights drear-y, I know my Sav - iour cares.

He cares.

No. 94. The Old-Fashioned Church.

Gypsy Simon Smith.

E. J. Bond.

1. There's an old-fashioned church where I worshipp'd of yore, With those whom I
2. O the bench-es were hard and the preach-er was old, But ma-ny a
3. How I long for that church and those meetings a-gain To hear moth-er's
4. As I wor-ship in church-es so state-ly and grand I long for the

lov'd who have gone on be-fore, 'Twas there in His tem-ple that God spoke to me,
sin-ner was brought to the fold, The sing-ing just seem'd to bring heav-en to me,
voice join in some sweet re-frain, Where dress did not mat-ter, all e-qual could be,
touch of a dear vanished hand, I think of God's a-cre where those dear to me

CHORUS.

In that old-fashioned church in the val - ley.
In that old-fashioned church in the val - ley.
In that old-fashioned church in the val - ley.
Lay at rest near the church in the val - ley.

O they told of a Sav-iour who

died on the tree, To purchase sal-va-tion for you and for me, 'Twas there at the

al-tar I found lib-er-ty In that old-fashioned church in the val-ley.

No. 95. When They Ring the Golden Bells.

DION DE MARBELLE.

1. There's a land be-yond the riv-er, That we call the sweet for-ev-er, And we
2. We shall know no sin nor sor-row, In that ha-ven of to-morrow, When our
3. When our days shall know their number, When in death we sweet-ly slumber, When the

on - ly reach that shore by faith's decree; One by one we'll gain the por-tals, There to
barque shall sail be-yond the sil - ver sea; We shall on - ly know the blessing Of our
King commands the spir-it to be free; Nev - er-more with an-guish la - den, We shall

dwell with the im-mortals, When they ring the golden bells for you and me.
Father's sweet caressing, When they ring the golden bells for you and me.
reach that love-ly ai-den, When they ring the golden bells for you and me.

you and me.

D. S.—yond the shining riv - er, When they ring the golden bells for you and me.

CHORUS.

Don't you hear the bells now ring-ing? Don't you hear the an - gels sing-ing? 'Tis the

D. S.

glo-ry hal - le - lu-jah Ju - bi - lee. In that far - off sweet forever, Just be -

Ju - bi - lee.

No. 96. God's Morning.

L. S. L.

DUET. *Espressivo.*

LIDA SHIVERS LEECH.

1. Are you un-done with the toil of the day, Al-most too wea-ry to
2. Close we shall stand by the pearl-y white throne, Where our Re-deem-er, the
3. O what re-joic-ing when friend meets with friend, In that bright cit-y where

think or to pray; Look to the hills where we'll gather some day, In the
Fa-ther's own Son, Then will re-ward us for la-bor well done, In the
joys nev-er end; Glad songs of praise and thanksgiv-ing will blend, In the

CHORUS.

morn-ing, God's beau-ti-ful morn-ing. In the morn-ing, God's beau-ti-ful

morn-ing, We shall meet in that wonder-ful day, With earth's tri-als all past,

rit.

We shall gath-er at last, In the morn-ing, God's beau-ti-ful morn-ing.

No. 97.

The Presence of God.

(To Lorena Hale, Washington Missionary College.)

A. V. MIDDLETON.

HAROLD AMADEUS MILLER.

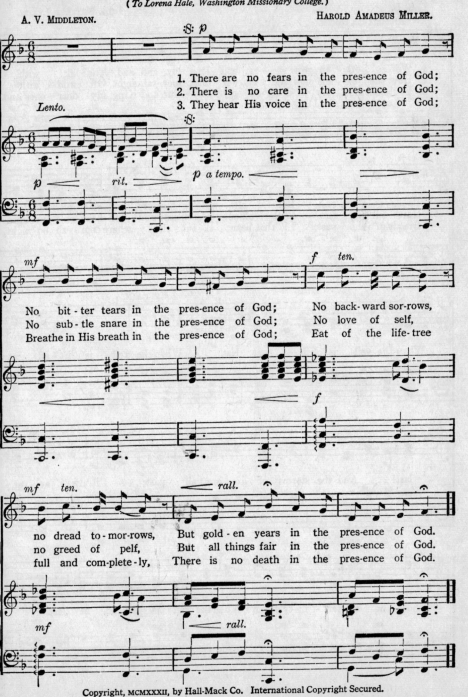

1. There are no fears in the pres-ence of God;
2. There is no care in the pres-ence of God;
3. They hear His voice in the pres-ence of God;

No bit-ter tears in the pres-ence of God; No back-ward sor-rows,
No sub-tle snare in the pres-ence of God; No love of self,
Breathe in His breath in the pres-ence of God; Eat of the life-tree

no dread to-mor-rows, But gold-en years in the pres-ence of God.
no greed of pelf, But all things fair in the pres-ence of God.
full and com-plete-ly, There is no death in the pres-ence of God.

No. 98. When the Veil is Lifted.

L. S. L.

LIDA SHIVERS LEECH.

Andante con espress.

1. We oft - en grow wea - ry, and lone - ly, and sad, The sky with
2. How the jew - els now hid from our weak mor - tal sight, Oft won with
3. I shall meet my Re-deem - er, my Sav - iour, and King, My dear ones and

clouds is o'er - cast, But all will be beau - ty, and glad - ness and love,
tears fall - ing fast, Will shine in each crown in yon heav - en's pure light,
friends of the past; In that beau - ti - ful cit - y, where com - eth no night,

REFRAIN.

When the veil is lift - ed at last. . . . When the veil is lift - ed at
at last.

last! . . . And the storms of life are all past; . . . I'll dwell ev - er-
at last. *all past;*

more, on e - ter - ni - ty's shore, When the veil is lift - ed at last. . . .
at last.

No. 99.   Looking This Way.

J. W. V.

J. W. Van DeVenter.

DUET.

1. O- ver the riv - er fa - ces I   see,   Fair as the morning, looking for   me;
2. Father and mother, safe in the   vale, Watch for the boatman, wait for the   sail,
3. Brother and sis - ter, gone to that clime, Wait for the oth-ers, coming some time;
4. Sweet lit-tle dar- ling, light of the home, Look-ing for some-one, beckon-ing   come;
5. Je- sus the Saviour, bright morning star, Look-ing for   lost ones, straying a - far;

Free from their sorrow, grief and de-spair,   Waiting and watching, pa-tient-ly   there.
Bear-ing the lov'd ones o - ver the   tide   In - to the har-bor, near to their   side.
Safe with the an- gels, whiter than snow, Watching for dear ones waiting be - low.
Bright as a sunbeam, pure as the   dew,   Anx-ious-ly look-ing, moth-er, for   you.
Hear the glad message; why will you roam?   Je- sus is call-ing, "Sinner, come home."

CHORUS.

Looking this way, yes, looking this   way; Loved ones are waiting, looking this   way;

Fair as the morning, bright as the   day, Dear ones in glo-ry looking this way.

Copyright, MDCCCXCV, by J. W. Van DeVenter. Used by per.

No. 100. Beyond the Clouds.

- W. C. POOLE.

B. D. ACKLEY.

1. Be-yond the clouds that drift above And sometimes veil from me,
2. Be-yond the clouds no shadows fall, No storm-y days are known;
3. Be-yond the clouds the other side Shines on with glo-ry bright,
4. Be-yond the clouds I have a home Where dear-est treasures are,

INST.

My Father's face, my Father's love, His matchless grace so free;
And love and light reign o-ver all, And God is on the throne;
As shines o'er all the sea so wide, The bil-lows in the light;
A-wait-ing me when I shall come Be-yond the clouds a - far;

As shines the sun with its bright flame, God lives and loves us just the same.
But this I know, that e'en to-day He guides the clouds upon their way.
And tho' a - while clouds hide their view, The light will come a-breaking thro'.
And this I know, no cloud a - bove Can keep from me the Father's love.

Beyond the Clouds.—Concluded.

REFRAIN.

And this I know, ... no clouds above   Can keep me from my Father's love.

And this I know,   no clouds above

No. 101.

Keep On Trying!

A. A. PAYN.

M. ISABELLE RITTER.

1. Are you seek-ing something on-ly God can give? Do not cease to pray,
2. Do you strive to con-quer some be-set-ting sin? Why should you de-spair?
3. If you feel a bur-den has been laid on you, More than you can bear,

For the Lord will hear you and the an-swer now   May be on its way.
Don't for-get that Je-sus is a Friend of yours,   He will an-swer pray'r.
Do not seek an-oth-er, he may have one too,   Go to God in pray'r.

CHORUS.

Keep on try-ing! Keep on pray-ing! Don't give up un-til you die!

For God will give you vic-to-ry,   You'll con-quer by and by.

No. 102. In the Land Where the Flowers Bloom Forever.

CAROLYN R. FREEMAN.

B. D. ACKLEY.

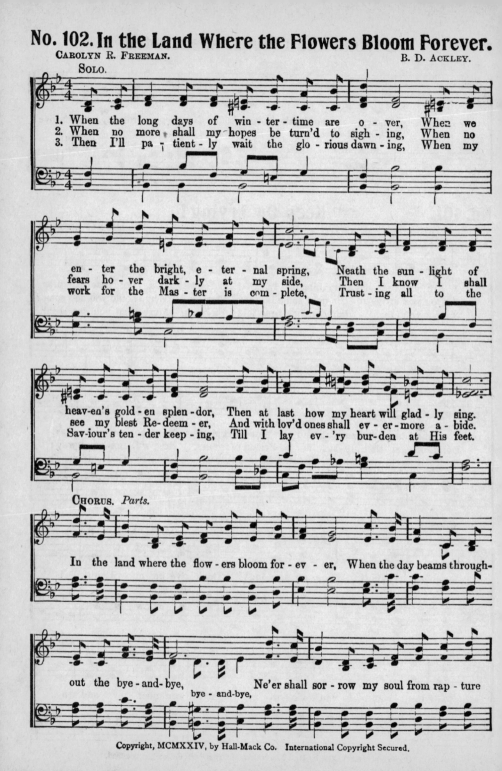

SOLO.

1. When the long days of win-ter-time are o-ver, When we
2. When no more shall my hopes be turn'd to sigh-ing, When no
3. Then I'll pa-tient-ly wait the glo-rious dawn-ing, When my

en-ter the bright, e-ter-nal spring, Neath the sun-light of
fears ho-ver dark-ly at my side, Then I know I shall
work for the Mas-ter is com-plete, Trust-ing all to the

heav-en's gold-en splen-dor, Then at last how my heart will glad-ly sing.
see my blest Re-deem-er, And with lov'd ones shall ev-er-more a-bide.
Sav-iour's ten-der keep-ing, Till I lay ev-'ry bur-den at His feet.

CHORUS. Parts.

In the land where the flow-ers bloom for-ev-er, When the day beams through-

out the bye-and-bye,
bye-and-bye,
Ne'er shall sor-row my soul from rap-ture

The Land Where the Flowers, etc.—Concluded.

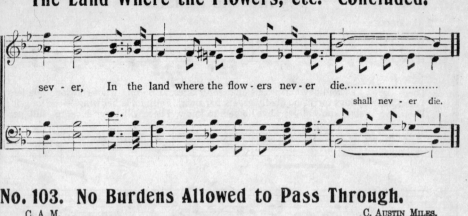

sev - er, In the land where the flow-ers nev-er die....................

shall nev - er die.

No. 103. No Burdens Allowed to Pass Through.

C. A. M.

C. Austin Miles.

1. I'm wea-ry of bear-ing my bur-den, But hope as my way I pur-sue,
2. I've en-tered dark valleys un-daunted, To take up my burden a-new,
3. My hand to my Saviour I've giv-en, To do what he asks me to do;
4. And then with the souls of the ransomed The journey complet-ed I'll view,

ritard.

I'll come to that gate where 'tis writ-ten, "No burdens allowed to pass through."
And look for the gate where 'tis writ-ten, "No burdens allowed to pass through."
Con-tent till he leads where 'tis writ-ten, "No burdens allowed to pass through."
With joy having pass'd where 'tis writ-ten, "No burdens allowed to pass through."

Chorus.

If sor-row or pain be my por-tion, To Je-sus I'll ev-er be true,

ritard.

Till I reach the fair gate where' tis written, "No burdens allowed to pass through."

No. 104.   Beyond the Sunset.

T. O. Chisholm.

B. D. Ackley.

1. There is a land beyond earth's changeful skies, Up-on whose bo-som fade-less
2. There hope springs forth and gladly greets her own, Faith folds her wings—the long, long
3. There we shall know all we have longed to know, There will our love to full per-

glo - ry lies; No sum-mer's heat, no win-ter's cold is there, No
flight is done—There, un-disturbed, Joy sings the whole day long, The
fec - tion grow; There we shall see the face of Christ, our Friend, And

Refrain.

oth - er land were half so wondrous fair.)
rap-t'rous strains of heav'n's re-demp-tion song. } Be-yond the sun-set and the
live with Him a life that has no end.)

ev'n - ing star, There is "a bet-ter coun-try"— bet - ter far, A land of

flowers, fruits and living streams, More fair, more bright, than all our fondest dreams.

our dreams.

No. 105.   The City of Gold.

L. S. L.

LIDA SHIVERS LEECH.

With expression.

1. I have read of a cit-y of gold, Which the Sav-iour has gone to pre-pare; But its glo-ries can nev-er be told, Till we meet 'neath its por-tals so fair.

2. I have read that its gates are of pearl, If I'm faith-ful they'll swing wide for me; I shall meet those who've gone on be-fore, And my Sav-iour with joy I shall see.

3. There's a man-sion for you and for me, And a robe that with joy we shall wear; We'll be safe in that cit-y of gold, From the world with its bur-den of care.

REFRAIN.

When I lay my sheaves at His feet, ... And I walk up the gold-paved street; . . . . Shall I meet you there? In the glo-ries to share, Of that beau-ti-ful cit-y of gold.

at His feet,   *gold-paved street;*

No. 106. Where the Years Shall Be Counted No More.

W. C. POOLE.   B. D. ACKLEY.

SOLO.

1. There are man-sions a-wait-ing for you and for me, When all of life's
2. There the glo-ry of Je-sus drives dark-ness a-way, And gives us the
3. There are bless-ings un-meas-ured be-yond the bright blue That fill all the

jour-ney is o'er, Where the shad-ows of part-ing will nev-er more be,
spring-time of youth. Where the Sav-iour for-ev-er makes end-less our day,
heav-en-ly shore. There is glo-ry e-ter-nal where live all the true,

CHORUS. PARTS.

And time shall be count-ed no more. . . . . ⎫
In heav-en-ly glad-ness and truth. . . . . ⎬ Where the years shall be counted no
Where years shall be count-ed no more. . . . . ⎭

more, . . . Where the years shall be counted no more, . . . We shall nev-er grow

no more,

SOLO. ad lib.

no more,

PARTS. rit.

old in that cit-y of gold, Where the years shall be counted no more. . . .

no more.

No. 107.

Some of These Days.

Frank L. Stanton.

DUET. SOP. AND ALTO.

J. Lincoln Hall.

1. Some of these days all the skies will be bright-er— Some of these days all the
2. Some of these days, in the des-erts up-spring-ing, Fountains shall flash, while the
3. Some of these days! Let us bear with our sor-row; Faith in the fu-ture—its

bur-dens be light-er; Hearts will be hap-pi-er, souls will be whit-er—
joy-bells are ring-ing, And all the world, with the birds, shall go sing-ing,
light we may bor-row; There will be joy in the gold-en to-mor-row,

CHORUS.

Some of these days, some of these days! Some of these days,............ some of these
Some of these days,

days,......... Skies will be bright-er some of these days;......... Some of these
some of these days, some of these days;

days all the bur-dens be light-er, Some of these days, some of these days!

No. 108. I Love to Think of Jesus.

C. Austin Miles.

Adam Geibel.

Solo, or All in Unison.

1. I love to think of Je-sus, who else could it be, Who could come down from
2. I love to think that He has giv-en me a part In par-don that He
3. I love to think of Je-sus when I am dis-trest, To think up-on His
4. I love to think of Him when tears of sor-row fall, To know that He has

heav'n to save a soul like me? To think of Him does not re-pay the
pur-chased with a bro-ken heart; And oft my eyes are fill'd with tears as
prom-ise brings a bliss-ful rest; In sor-row, pain and an-guish He is
suf-fered and He knows it all; It gives me strength to bear my bur-dens

debt I owe, I'll do my best my grat-i-tude to show..........
I re-call What He has done for me, and for us all..........
near I know, It is no won-der that I love Him so..........
nor com-plain, I nev-er yet have called to Him in vain,..........

Two-Part Chorus.*

I love.......... to think of Je-sus,.......... I
I love to think of Je-sus and His love for me; My

love.......... to think of Je-sus,
soul is lost in won-der that such love could be; I've known the love of moth-er, Of

I Love to Think of Jesus.—Concluded.

Parts. ritard.

sis-ter, friend and brother, Like Je-sus there's no other, He's more than all to me.

No Tears in the Sky.

No. 109.

C. E. S.

CHARLES E. SMITH.

With feeling.

1. O there's no sor-row in heav-en, No part-ing and no good-bye;
2. O there's no sad dis-ap-point-ment, No eyes fill'd with tears to dry,
3. Up there no hearts that are bro-ken, There no one to breathe a sigh,
4. Here hearts are sorrow'd by sad-ness, For lov'd ones and friends must die;

To those with sins all for-giv-en, There'll be no tears in the sky.
For there will be glad con-tent-ment, There are no tears in the sky.
No un-kind word will be spo-ken, There'll be no tears in the sky.
But there is sunshine and glad-ness, There'll be no tears in the sky.

CHORUS.

No sor-row is found in that cit-y, No heartache and no good-bye;

rit.

For all will be bright in that cit-y of light, For there are no tears in the sky.

No. 110. Sometime, Somewhere.

D. C. MacLeod.　　　　　　　　　　　　　　　　　　Adam Geibel.

1. Sometime, somewhere, beyond earth's fleeting shad - ows, We'll meet our bless - ed
2. Sometime, somewhere, we'll drink from heav'nly fountains, Where pure, un - fail - ing
3. Sometime, somewhere, we'll dwell in lands of sun - shine, Where bit - ter pain and
4. Sometime, somewhere, we'll wear a crown of glo - ry, And dwell in heav'n - ly

Saviour face to face; Sometime, somewhere, we'll join the throngs in glo-ry, And sing the
streams for-ev - er flow; Sometime, somewhere, the Bread of Life we'll gather, The pangs of
part-ing are unknown; Sometime, somewhere, we'll dry those tears of sorrow, The burdens
mansions fair and grand; Sometime, somewhere, midst glorious scenes we'll wander, The dark night

Chorus.

song of wondrous love and grace.
earth - ly hun-ger ne'er to know.
gone, the hours of dark-ness flown.
pass'd, we've reach'd that happy land.

Not now nor here, ... but aft - er
Not now nor here,

while . . . . . The joys of heav'n with lov'd ones we shall share; . . . . . Then we shall
but aft - er while　　　　　　　　　　　　　　　　　　　　　yes, we shall share;

meet, ... to part no more, ... Sometime, somewhere, sometime, somewhere.
Then we shall meet,　　　　　　to part no more,　　　　　　　　　　　　somewhere.

No. 111.   The Master's Garden.

GRACE GORDON.   ADAM GEIBEL.

Solo or Duet.

1. In the garden of the Master, Bloom the flow'rs so bright and fair, Which his hand in love has
2. In the gar-den of the Mas-ter, Lillies bloom in white ar-ray, Breathing forth a ho-ly
3. In the gar-den of the Mas-ter All is joy and endless peace, For his love shall ev-er

planted, Which He guards with tend'rest care. Naught can harm the fragrant blossoms, Wintry
in - cense, In the breeze their censers sway, Like the throngs of shining an-gels, By the
cher - ish, And his care can nev-er cease, There be-yond the shining por-tal, In the

storms can never blight, For the sunshine of his presence, Sheds for aye its wondrous light.
bright and jasper throne, In the gar-den of the Master, When they bloom for him alone.
realms of light a-bove, Earthly flow'rs shall bloom immortal In the gar-den of his love.

CHORUS.

When we meet in heaven's gar-den, When the gates are o-pen wide,

When we meet, we meet in heaven's garden, When the gates, the gates are o-pen, o-pen wide,

We shall gath - er all our lil - lies, Growing at our Saviour's side.

We shall gath-er, gath-er all our lil - lies, Growing, grow-ing at our Saviour's side.

The Upper Window.

J. B.

Rev. JOHN BIERI, D.D.

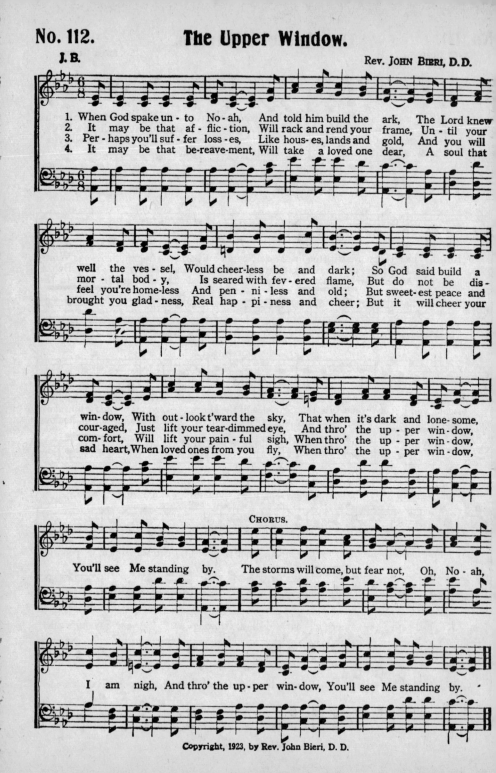

1. When God spake un - to No - ah, And told him build the ark, The Lord knew
2. It may be that af - flic - tion, Will rack and rend your frame, Un - til your
3. Per - haps you'll suf - fer loss - es, Like hous - es, lands and gold, And you will
4. It may be that be-reave-ment, Will take a loved one dear, A soul that

well the ves - sel, Would cheer-less be and dark; So God said build a
mor - tal bod - y, Is seared with fev - ered flame, But do not be dis-
feel you're home-less And pen - ni - less and old; But sweet-est peace and
brought you glad - ness, Real hap - pi - ness and cheer; But it will cheer your

win - dow, With out - look t'ward the sky, That when it's dark and lone-some,
cour-aged, Just lift your tear-dimmed eye, And thro' the up - per win - dow,
com- fort, Will lift your pain - ful sigh, When thro' the up - per win - dow,
sad heart, When loved ones from you fly, When thro' the up - per win - dow,

CHORUS.

You'll see Me standing by. The storms will come, but fear not, Oh, No - ah,

I am nigh, And thro' the up - per win - dow, You'll see Me standing by.

No. 113.

Just the Same.

Col. J. C. ADDIE.

W. H. JUDE.
(Arr. by Clyde Willard.)

SOLO, *or all in Unison.*

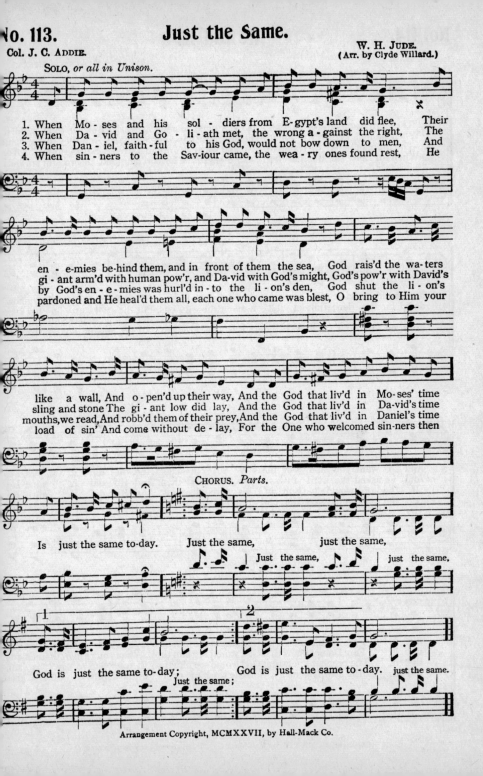

1. When Mo - ses and his sol - diers from E - gypt's land did flee, Their
2. When Da - vid and Go - li - ath met, the wrong a - gainst the right, The
3. When Dan - iel, faith - ful to his God, would not bow down to men, And
4. When sin - ners to the Sav - iour came, the wea - ry ones found rest, He

en - e - mies be - hind them, and in front of them the sea, God rais'd the wa - ters
gi - ant arm'd with human pow'r, and Da - vid with God's might, God's pow'r with David's
by God's en - e - mies was hurl'd in - to the li - on's den, God shut the li - on's
pardoned and He heal'd them all, each one who came was blest, O bring to Him your

like a wall, And o - pen'd up their way, And the God that liv'd in Mo - ses' time
sling and stone The gi - ant low did lay, And the God that liv'd in Da - vid's time
mouths, we read, And robb'd them of their prey, And the God that liv'd in Daniel's time
load of sin' And come without de - lay, For the One who welcomed sin - ners then

CHORUS. *Parts.*

Is just the same to-day. Just the same, just the same,
Just the same, just the same.

1
God is just the same to - day;
Just the same;

2
God is just the same to - day. just the same.

Arrangement Copyright, MCMXXVII, by Hall-Mack Co.

No. 114.

He Did It.

C. A. M.

C. AUSTIN MILES.

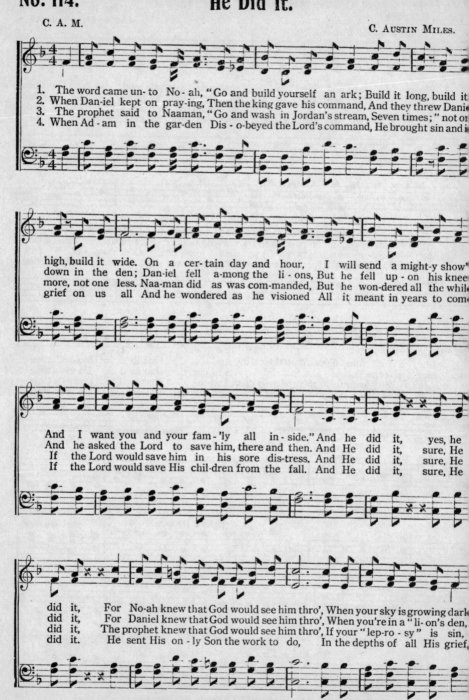

1. The word came un-to No-ah, "Go and build yourself an ark; Build it long, build it
2. When Dan-iel kept on pray-ing, Then the king gave his command, And they threw Danie
3. The prophet said to Naaman, "Go and wash in Jordan's stream, Seven times;" not on
4. When Ad-am in the gar-den Dis-o-beyed the Lord's command, He brought sin and i

high, build it wide. On a cer-tain day and hour, I will send a might-y show'
down in the den; Dan-iel fell a-mong the li-ons, But he fell up-on his knee
more, not one less. Naa-man did as was com-manded, But he won-dered all the whil
grief on us all And he wondered as he visioned All it meant in years to com

And I want you and your fam-'ly all in-side." And he did it, yes, he
And he asked the Lord to save him, there and then. And He did it, sure, He
If the Lord would save him in his sore dis-tress. And He did it, sure, He
If the Lord would save His chil-dren from the fall. And He did it, sure, He

did it, For No-ah knew that God would see him thro', When your sky is growing dark
did it, For Daniel knew that God would see him thro', When you're in a "li-on's den,
did it, The prophet knew that God would see him thro', If your "lep-ro-sy" is sin,
did it. He sent His on-ly Son the work to do, In the depths of all His grief,

He Did It.—Concluded.

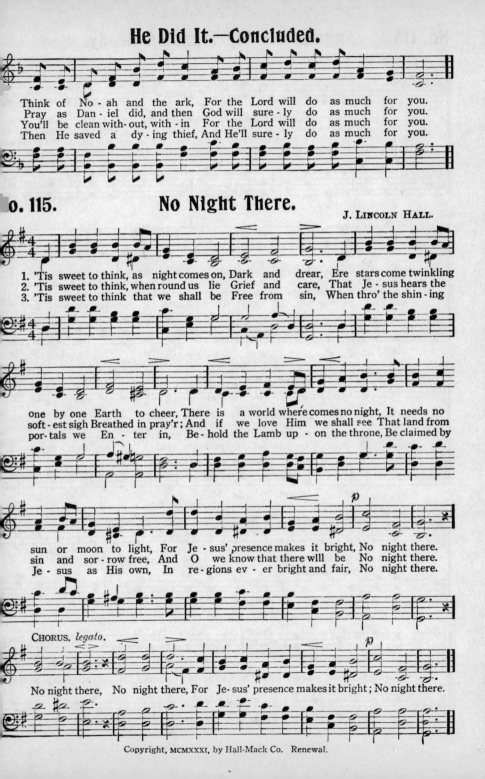

Think of No-ah and the ark, For the Lord will do as much for you.
Pray as Dan-iel did, and then God will sure-ly do as much for you.
You'll be clean with-out, with-in For the Lord will do as much for you.
Then He saved a dy-ing thief, And He'll sure-ly do as much for you.

No. 115. No Night There.

J. LINCOLN HALL.

1. 'Tis sweet to think, as night comes on, Dark and drear, Ere stars come twinkling
2. 'Tis sweet to think, when round us lie Grief and care, That Je-sus hears the
3. 'Tis sweet to think that we shall be Free from sin, When thro' the shin-ing

one by one Earth to cheer, There is a world where comes no night, It needs no
soft-est sigh Breathed in pray'r; And if we love Him we shall see That land from
por-tals we En-ter in, Be-hold the Lamb up-on the throne, Be claimed by

sun or moon to light, For Je-sus' presence makes it bright, No night there.
sin and sor-row free, And O we know that there will be No night there.
Je-sus as His own, In re-gions ev-er bright and fair, No night there.

CHORUS. *legato.*

No night there, No night there, For Je-sus' presence makes it bright; No night there.

No. 116.   Angels, Get My Mansion Ready.

Rev. JOHNSON OATMAN, Jr.

C. AUSTIN MILES.

1. O - ver yonder stands the mansion Christ prepared for me, God ordained that I shou
2. Pur - er are the joys up yon-der than the halls of mirth, Grander are the songs e
3. Tho' a pil-grim I have wandered in the val - ley here, Now un - to the bless-ed
4. When my work be-low is end - ed and my race is run, I will hear my Saviou

have it from e - ter - ni - ty; And I'll send a pray'r be - fore me, ere I
ter - nal than the songs of earth; Sweet-er is the bread of heav - en than the
homeland I am draw-ing near; Soon a - mid these scenes of sor - row I will
call - ing at the set of sun; Then I'll send a mes-sage up - ward, past yor

cross the foam, "An - gels, get my mansion read - y, I am com - ing home."
hon - ey comb, An - gels, get my mansion read - y, I am com - ing home.
cease to roam, An - gels, get my mansion read - y, I am com - ing home.
vault - ed dome, "An - gels, get my mansion read - y, I am com - ing home."

CHORUS.

I am com - ing home to heav - en, with the an - gels there to dwell, I am

com-ing home to glo - ry, where I'll nev - er say fare-well; I am com - ing to that

Angels, Get My Mansion Ready.—Concluded.

cit - y, nev - er-more to roam, An-gels, get my mansion read-y, I am com-ing home.

No. 117. He Knows, Loves, Forgives.

Rev. FREDERICK BLASER. C. AUSTIN MILES.

1. How sweet the thought my Fa-ther *knows.* My storm-y path, be - set with woes;
2. In - spir-ing thought my Fa-ther *loves,* My ev -'ry act His great heart moves,
3. Sub-lime the thought that God *for-gives* The man who His great love re - ceives,

But sweet-er far, His word de-clares, He's "mind-ful of His own" and *cares.*
Tho' dark the way, tho' far I roam His win-some love will guide me home.
Blots out his sin, re-moves the shame And writes in heav-en a "bet - ter name."

REFRAIN.

My Fa-ther *knows,* O yes, and cares, My Fa-ther *loves,* each bur - den shares,

rit.

My Fa-ther *waits,* O wondrous grace! And I shall see Him face to face.

Nothing Satisfies But Jesus.

H. L.

HALDOR LILLENAS.

DUET.—Tenor and Alto. (Small notes if Soprano and Alto.)

1. Noth-ing sat - is - fies but Je - sus, All the world is emp - ti - ness, All its
2. Noth-ing sat - is - fies but Je - sus, Earthly treas- ure must de - cay, Here to-
3. Noth-ing sat - is - fies but Je - sus, He can heal the bro - ken heart, Speaking

glit - ter and its glo - ry Can-not sat - is - fy or bless; All its gai - e - ty and
day and gone to-morrow, Fleeting things that pass a-way; But His love is true and
words of ho - ly comfort, Bidding anx - ious fears depart; In His pres-ence I find

splen-dor Have to me dis-taste-ful grown; Noth-ing sat - is - fies but Je - sus,
con-stant, He for - ev - er is the same, Noth-ing sat - is - fies but Je - sus,
shel - ter, When the billows round me roll, Noth-ing sat - is - fies but Je - sus,

CHORUS.

I am His and His a - lone. }
Glo - ry to His matchless name! } Noth-ing sat - is - fies but Je - sus, Fain my
He who ran- som'd my poor soul. }

soul to Him would fly; He will sat - is - fy my longing, He will all my needs supply.

No. 119.

My Mother's Song.

(To Mother.)

Maud Frazer Jackson.

Harold Amadeus Miller.

Meditatively.

1. I heard a song that touched my heart, And filled my eyes with tears, It
2. How sweet the words that gave me hope, That I might be re-stored,— "Come,
3. I seemed to hear her gen-tle voice As in the long a-go,— "Plunge

was the song my mother sang, In long de-part-ed years.
ev - 'ry soul by sin oppressed, There's mer - cy with the Lord."
now in - to the crimson flood, That wash - es white as snow."

rit. e dim.

REFRAIN. (Stockton.)

"On - ly trust Him, on - ly trust Him, On - ly trust Him now;

rit.

He will save you, He will save you, He will save you now."

rit.

No. 120. A Mother's Prayer.

C. A. M.

C. Austin Miles.

Solo. *Unison throughout. Slowly.*

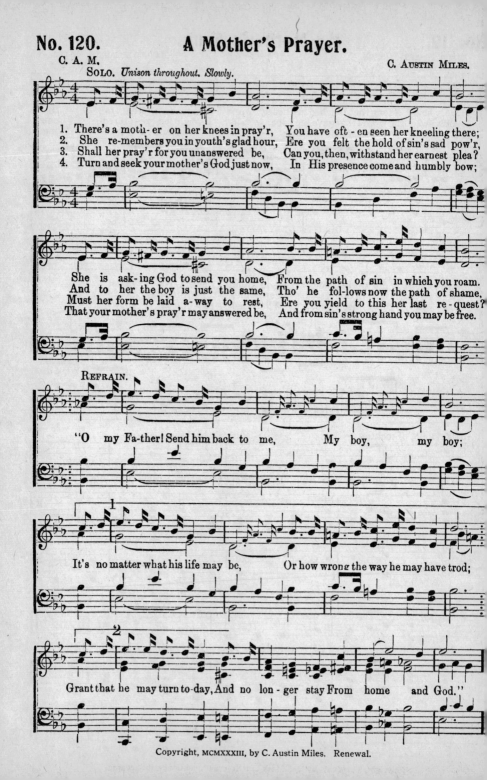

1. There's a moth-er on her knees in pray'r, You have oft-en seen her kneeling there;
2. She re-members you in youth's glad hour, Ere you felt the hold of sin's sad pow'r,
3. Shall her pray'r for you unanswered be, Can you, then, withstand her earnest plea?
4. Turn and seek your mother's God just now, In His presence come and humbly bow;

She is ask-ing God to send you home, From the path of sin in which you roam.
And to her the boy is just the same, Tho' he fol-lows now the path of shame,
Must her form be laid a-way to rest, Ere you yield to this her last re-quest?
That your mother's pray'r may answered be, And from sin's strong hand you may be free.

REFRAIN.

"O my Fa-ther! Send him back to me, My boy, my boy;

It's no matter what his life may be, Or how wrong the way he may have trod;

Grant that he may turn to-day, And no lon-ger stay From home and God."

No. 121. Mother's Religion.

C. W. D.

CHAS. W. DRISKELL.

SOLO OR DUET.

1. I was young, but I re-mem-ber; as I sat at mother's knee, How she
2. Years have pass'd since mother's spir-it winged its flight to yon bright shore, I have
3. When the shad-ows gath-er round me, at the clos-ing of life's day, Then the

taught me from the Bi-ble, of Christ who died for me, She said, my boy, trust
tast-ed life's pure fountain, am saved for ev-er-more, When-e'er I meet with
Old Time Re-lig-ion will be my guide and stay, When I cross death's turbid

Je-sus, his grace will set you free, Seek the Old Time Re-lig-ion, For 'tis
tri-als, I now each day can see That the Old Time Re-lig-ion, Still is
riv-er my Saviour's face I see Then the Old Time Re-lig-ion Will be

CHORUS.

good e-nough for me. 'Tis the Old Time Re-lig-ion, 'tis the Old Time Re-

lig-ion 'Tis the Old Time Re-lig-ion; And 'tis good e-nough for me.

No. 122. Memories.

C. A. M.

C. Austin Miles.

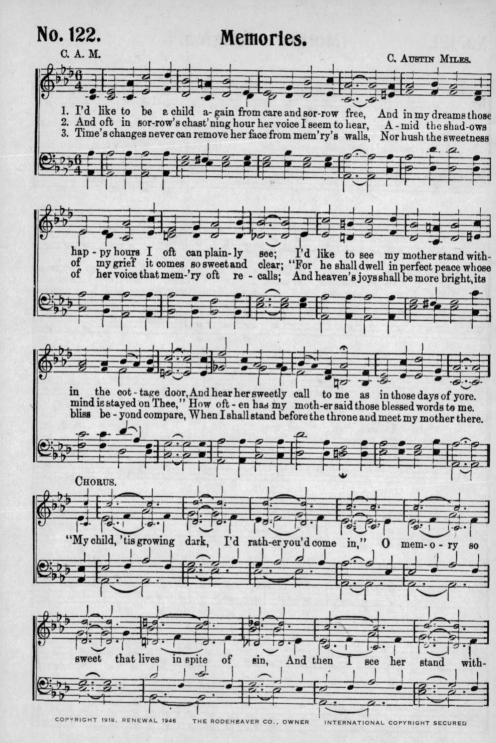

1. I'd like to be a child a-gain from care and sor-row free, And in my dreams those
2. And oft in sor-row's chast'ning hour her voice I seem to hear, A-mid the shad-ows
3. Time's changes never can remove her face from mem'ry's walls, Nor hush the sweetness

hap-py hours I oft can plain-ly see; I'd like to see my mother stand with-
of my grief it comes so sweet and clear; "For he shall dwell in perfect peace whose
of her voice that mem'ry oft re-calls; And heaven's joys shall be more bright, its

in the cot-tage door, And hear her sweetly call to me as in those days of yore.
mind is stayed on Thee," How oft-en has my moth-er said those blessed words to me.
bliss be-yond compare, When I shall stand before the throne and meet my mother there.

CHORUS.

"My child, 'tis growing dark, I'd rath-er you'd come in," O mem-o-ry so

sweet that lives in spite of sin, And then I see her stand with-

Memories.—Concluded.

in the o-pen door; I'd give the world if I could hear My mother's voice once more.

No. 123.   Can a Boy Forget His Mother?

J. H. W,

Prof. J. H. WEBER.

1. Can a boy for-get his mother's pray'r, When he has wandered, God knows where?
2. Can a boy for-get his mother's face, Whose heart was kind and filled with grace?
3. Can a boy for-get his mother's door, From which he wandered years be-fore?
4. Can a boy for-get that she is dead, Tho' ma-ny years have passed and fled?

It's down the path of death and shame, But mother's pray'rs are heard the same!
Her lov-ing voice it ech-oes sweet; She waits, she longs her boy to meet!
With tears and sighs she said, "Good-bye, Meet me, my boy, be-yond the sky!"
Those tears, that pray'r, that sweet "Good-bye;" She waits to wel-come thee on high!

CHORUS.

Come back, my boy, come back, I say, And walk now in thy moth-er's way!

Come back, my boy, come back, I say, And walk now in thy mother's way.

Copyright, MDCCCLXXXIX, by Prof. J.H. Weber. By per.

No. 124.   My Mother's Prayer.

J. W. Van DeVenter.

W. S. Weeden.

1. I nev-er can for-get the day I heard my moth-er kind-ly say,
2. I nev-er can for-get the voice That al-ways made my heart re-joice;
3. Tho' years have gone, I can't for-get Those words of love— I hear them yet;
4. I nev-er can for-get the hour I felt the Sav-iour's cleansing pow'r,

"You're leav-ing now my ten-der care; Re-mem-ber, child, your mother's pray'r."
Tho' I have wandered God knows where, Still I re-mem-ber mother's pray'r.
I see her by the old arm chair, My moth-er dear, in humble pray'r.
My sin and guilt he can-celed there, 'Twas there he an-swered mother's pray'r.

CHORUS.

1-3. Whene'er I think of her so dear, I feel her an-gel spir-it near;
4. Oh praise the Lord for sav-ing grace! We'll meet up yon-der face to face;

A voice comes float-ing on the air, Re-mind-ing me of moth-er's pray'r.
The home a-bove to-geth-er share, In an-swer to my moth-er's pray'r.

Copyright, MDCCCXCV, by J. W. Van DeVenter. Used by permission.

No. 125. My Mother's Old Bible is True.

(Dedicated to the Men and Religion Forward Movement.)

E. E. HEWITT.

Tenors and Basses, or All in Unison, or Solo.

ADAM GEIBEL.

1. I've found that earth's wa - ters will ne'er sat - is - fy, I sought for re -
2. I turned to the Bi - ble, glad ti - dings I read, Of riv - ers un -
3. I read of the mer - cy that brought him to die, To save guilt - y
4. A - way with the fountains that shine but to mock, A - way with earth's

fresh-ing and cheer;... Its cisterns were brok-en, its fountains were dry,
fail - ing and bright;... Of Christ the Good Shepherd, who safely hath led
sin - ners like me;... That now he is liv-ing in glo-ry on high,
per - ish-ing toys;... I drink of the wa - ter that flows from the rock,

CHORUS.

Its joys like the dews dis-ap - pear....
His flock by the streams of de - light....
My more than a broth - er to be....
I feast up - on in - fi - nite joys....

My mother's old Bi - ble is

true;... From cov - er to cov - er, all true!... A message of love,
is true;   all true!

'Twas sent from a - bove; My moth-er's old Bi - ble is true...
is true.

INDEX